2020:

The year that tried to kill me

A True Story

By Oliver Morrison

Table of Contents

Introduction

They say life begins at forty but for me it nearly ended or, at least, that's one way to look at it anyway. Who am I? I'm just a regular guy, trying to live an ordinary life who survived a series of extraordinary events that can only be described as attempts on my life by natural causes.

Born in 1980, I'm one of the last members of generation X.

A generation that remembers a time before mobile phones.

A generation who could entertain ourselves with a stick and a drinks can, a generation who, if you wanted to call a friend and they lived in the same village, you would only have to dial three numbers from a land line.

A generation who remembers having only four TV channels, a generation who was rewarded for achieving accomplishments and not just for turning up, and a generation who, as kids, if you threw a tantrum or back chatted your mum you wouldn't be sat down to talk about your feelings like the privileged kids of today, oh no, you would get one of three prizes, prize one the slipper, prize two the spatula or prize three, my mum's behaviour correctional tool of choice, the wooden spoon.

I can tell you one thing though, it worked. I think the older generation used to call it 'character building'.

Anyway, as I said, I'm just a regular guy, trying to live an ordinary life.

The trouble is nothing in my life is ordinary!

Take where I'm from. Now to any normal person that would be an easy question to answer, but for me it's a bloody mine field. I live in a small town on the border between Wales and England called Oswestry. It is right on the welsh border, and in fact it changed hands between Welsh and English many times during the middle ages till it eventually was deemed to be English.

I haven't always lived there though. I've lived all over the country and all over the world in fact. My dad worked in the oil industry, so he moved about a lot. I was actually born in Venezuela, South America, before moving to Huston, Texas, when I was a baby and spent the first 6 years of my life living state side. We eventually moved to the U.K, where my dad is originally from.

My mother, on the other hand, was from Thailand, which is where I get my darker complexion and south East Asian features from.

We moved about all over the U.K before settling in Oswestry nearly 18 years later.

The family had changed along the way as I now had a brother, a sister, and a step mum. Mum and Dad divorced back in the mid nineties and then my mum lost her battle with cancer in 2001. Oswestry is where I've lived all my adult life.

I've been here over twenty years.

I have many friends which I have known over the twenty years, and the bond with them is very strong. So, if I get asked the question, 'where are you from?' I would say Oswestry, but I've learnt over the years, especially my younger days, that people sometimes do not actually want to know where I'm from.

They want the answer to a different question entirely.

Because when I answer them, it's not the answer they are looking for and they'll follow up with, "No, I mean where were you born?"

So, when I tell them Venezuela in South America, they look at me with confusion, as if I've said the wrong answer.

Then I'll get a "You don't look like you're from South America?" Which is when it becomes apparent what they are actually trying to ask me and had been for the last 15 minutes is *what is your ethnic background?* So, then I have to explain to them that my dad is English and my mum is Thai and that I am the product of such union.

Living in a small farmers market town on the welsh border there wasn't a great deal of ethnic diversity, to say the least, but I was never victim to any discrimination although, there were the odd accounts of small mindedness, mainly from older generations. I dealt with it all with humour and it wasn't ever malicious but based in ignorance.

An old boy once asked me where I was from and knowing full well what he meant, I didn't give him the answer he was looking for. I fucked with him and said in the broadest old school Oswestrian accent "I'm from Oswestry monner," and walked off as he went cross eyed and tilted his head slightly, his brain not being able to compute the voice coming from the foreigner in front of him.

We're a hardy bunch from Oswestry, always the underdog. I remember going out drinking as a young adult. If we went 15 minutes north to Wrexham, which is in Wales, they used to run us out saying we were English scum, and if we went 15 minutes south to Shrewsbury, which like Oswestry is in England, they would run us out calling us Welsh sheep shaggers!

The odds always seemed to be against us, but it was never a deterrent.

This is why I think there is a close-knit community feel to this little farmers market town I call home.

Nearly twenty years I had lived in Oswestry before I moved back to my dad and Step mum's house, in a little village just outside of the town. The pressure of things in my life became overwhelming and you know when you just need to recalibrate your life.

Well, that happened to me.

It was as if one day I was in my early twenties, with my whole life ahead of me, and before I knew it, I was the wrong end of thirty, single and drowning in debt, just going through the motions of a mundane existence. I was just coasting through life, trying to keep my head above the water. I was not in a good place at all, but what can I say, shit happens. Something had to give, which is why I decided to move back in with my parents and revaluate my life.

Time is such a precious commodity, it's a luxury that I think so many of us find too easy to take for granted.

That's why I have learnt it is so important to live your best life and not be constraint from the fear of change, the fear of rejection or the fear of failure.

Change is ok it's a natural part of progression.

Rejection is ok once your over that initial hurt you can evaluate your situation and feel motivated to do better it can also urge you to explore a different path in life.

Failure is ok it's a natural phase of learning, we cannot learn without failing. If you're not careful time will pass you by in an instant.

Everything moved in the right direction for me, living back at my parents. I kept my head down and was getting myself out of debt. Don't get me wrong, moving back to my parents at nearly forty is not something I'm proud of, but sometimes you have to put your pride in your pocket, which is a very hard thing to do. But as they say, everything happens for a reason.

Call it fate, if you will, because if I hadn't been living with my parents, I don't believe I would be alive to tell this story.

Now the events I'm about to relay to you are so outrageous that you wouldn't believe they could happen to one person, let alone happen in one year, which is why I had to write about it.

I used to think that what I went through was the most challenging thing in my life, but as time went on I thought I could take that challenge to the next level. If I can inspire at least one person not to give up in the face of adversity, even when things seem to be at their upmost difficult, then surely that would be a positive impact to have come out of the horrific ordeal I went through.

There were many ways I could have written this book, but I thought it best to be written as true to my personality as possible, which can be quite cynical, but I always try to see the good in every situation. I also try to make light of bad situations when I can, especially if those bad situations involve me.

This is a warts and all account of the most harrowing year of my life which brought me face to face with death itself. Apologies in advance to my parents for the gratuitous profanity laden content you are about to encounter.

Side Splitting Fun

Ouch!

To recollect the bizarre events of 2020 first we have to go back to the setup of my unfortunate demise.

It was mid December 2019 when I came down with what seemed to be the mother of all colds, which was typical because it was the Christmas holidays, my brother and his girlfriend were visiting, and I was feeling ruff as a bear's arse.

Runny nose check, cold sweats check, fever check, aching body check, constant cough check.

I had all the symptoms of a cold like flu, great! After a couple of weeks, some of the symptoms subsided, but I was still weak, and I couldn't shake the cough. In fact, come New Year's Eve, I was still feeling that rough so I stayed in instead of going out with friends to celebrate.

It's officially 2020.

January 2nd which was a Thursday, and I still felt like death warmed up, so I had the first few days off work with the mindset of starting back after a long weekend of rest.

Monday came round and I still didn't feel 100 percent, with a rasping chesty cough that I just couldn't shake. I got through Monday, just, but I still felt drained and was coughing like there was no tomorrow, so I had an early night, hoping the extra rest would make me feel better.

Tuesday morning came around, and after another night of tossing and turning and coughing, I dragged my carcass out of bed and went for my morning shower.

I was that tired I went in to autopilot. I brushed my teeth first, and then I started having another coughing fit as I went to step in the shower. And right at the end of the vicious coughing fit, on the last cough, I got an almighty searing pain in my left side under my armpit. It was so severe it stopped me in my tracks. I thought I was actually in shock.

I remember thinking *What...... The.......Fuck was that?!*

It felt like I had taken a running toe punt kick to the ribs. A few more seconds passed, and I remembered to start breathing again, which didn't come without complication, as every breath I took brought a flood of pain to me.

For fuck's sake, I haven't got time for this shit, I thought. I needed to get ready for work.

So, I finished my shower, got ready, and drove to work, which was an experience in itself, as every movement I made was agony.

I work for a small, family run business that specialises in the ground care industry, selling a range of ground care equipment including lawn mowers from domestic to professional multi gang mowers, as used by councils and golf courses, Quad bikes and utility vehicles used mainly by the farming community to Golf buggies.

By the time I got to the office, I was sweating, clutching my side, and very pale.

I walked in and my work colleague just looked at me like a mangy wet dog had just walked in the office and said, "What the hell is wrong with you?"

I explained to her what happened as I punched the digits to my doctor's surgery on my desk phone. Luckily, I got an appointment straight away.

My appointment was with a female doctor who I hadn't seen before, as my usual doctor was unavailable at such short notice.

After explaining what happened to me, she proceeded to examine the area in question, poking and prodding my side, which sent waves of nausea through me.

Jesus! Why does my pain threshold have be so high? I'd much rather be unconscious now! I thought.

After examining me, the doctor gave me her verdict.

"Well, Mr Morrison, it looks like you may have fractured or damaged a rib. I am going to have to refer you for an X-Ray. The soonest I can book you in is next Monday."

Next Monday being 6 days away.

Nothing like rushing the job, hey! I thought.

Her parting comment, as I got up to leave was, "In the meantime, take some paracetamol to manage the pain."

Awesome, I thought, *Paracetamol. You know that drug that does absolutely fuck all for pain! Yeah, thanks Doc.*

Needless to say, I didn't go back to work that day, or for the rest of the week in fact. I went home and rested. Well, attempted to rest, as all I could do was lie on my back and not move an inch, as every time I did, I'd be in agony.

I dosed up on Paracetamol and Ibuprofen over the next few days which toned the pain down from excruciating to a constant pain. I stayed in bed for about 4 days before I was up and about again.

It was the Sunday when my friends talked me into going for a walk with them.

It's just a cracked rib, I told myself, just got to suck it up and soldier on.

"The fresh air will do you some good!" they said.

Another handful of painkillers and a 5km trek later and...............nope! I didn't even feel marginally better. In fact, I felt worse. My side was thumping with each breathe I took, my legs were aching, and my feet felt like they'd been worn away to stumps...*Good times!* I thought.

After another restless night it was finally Monday and I was booked in at the local orthopaedic hospital for my X-Ray. *At last*, I thought *I can find out what's going on with me.* Well, if only that was the case.

After I had my X-Ray, the nurse who did it thanked me for coming and said they would forward the results to my GP and they should have them in about a week.

Well, that was as about as helpful as tits on a bull, I thought, and drove home still perplexed about what the hell was wrong with me.

That's new?

On Tuesday morning, I begrudgingly got up and coasted through my work day powered by painkillers and sheer determination.

It felt like I got through the day by the skin of my teeth.

I went home, had a bite to eat, and passed out on my bed from the exhaustion of constantly being in pain.

It was about 3am the next morning when I was rudely awakened by a new excruciating pain and having to gasp for air. The pain had changed. It was deeper inside the left chest area and all I could do was take short gasps of air, every time being rewarded with a sharp stabbing inside of me.

I sat up in bed, thinking *Shit! This is new, Fuck! Fuck! Fuck! What am I going to do? I can't wake up my dad and step mum, it's 3am! I'll have to wait for the walk-in centre to open at 8am and go there; yeah, they'll know what to do!*

So, like an idiot, I sat there gasping for air till 7.50am, when I got in my car and drove to the walk-in centre.

It's a good job it was less than a mile from where I lived, because if driving was difficult before, it was near impossible now, but I managed to do it without causing an accident. Which would have been the cherry on the cake with the week I was having.

I hobbled to the reception and asked if I can be seen by someone.

"Not a problem please take a seat in the waiting area," the receptionist said.

It wasn't long before my name was called, as I was the only person in there at 8am.

Off I went, into a treatment room with a nurse and explained to her what was happening with me and she told me to take my shirt off and had a listen around my chest and back with a stethoscope.

When she finished examining me, she told me with wide eyes that I should have called an ambulance, but as my Doctors surgery was only across the road, she was going to refer me to them.

So, back in my car I got to drive literally 30 seconds across the road to my doctor's surgery where I was seen straight away because the walk-in centre had already rung ahead and briefed them.

I was examined again by a doctor and his stethoscope and he quickly confirmed that I needed to go to hospital straight away and an ambulance was called for me.

I was left in a treatment room by myself to wait for the ambulance and I thought, *Well, this is shit isn't it! With everything that has happened in my life, nothing really surprises me anymore.*

Honestly, I could get abducted by aliens and it would just be another day at the office. I think I've become desensitised to extreme situations and I just deal with whatever shit life throws at me and I try to see the funny side of things.

Mainly because if I didn't laugh about it, I think I'd cry.

After my little ride in the ambulance, I arrived at Shrewsbury hospital where the paramedics handed me over and I was given a bed in the respiratory ward. I was seen by another doctor who took some blood, ordered a chest X-Ray, and gave me some paracetamol, which I smirk at, but still take it none the less.

"But you've already had an X-Ray," I hear you say, and yes, I have, but that was at the local orthopaedic hospital and I'm now at The Royal Shrewsbury hospital and different NHS entities don't seem to communicate to each other because that would be too easy!

The hospital was pretty busy, and I was put in a ward with five other beds and all of them were full. Half an hour past when two nurses wheeled in a mobile X-Ray machine.

All I had to do was sit upright in my bed while they manoeuvred the machine in front of my chest and took the scan. I just laid back to wait. I found that if I lay as still as possible, it would minimise the pain.

After what felt like hours, the specialist consultant came round to give me the verdict.

"Well, Mr Morrison, on examining your X-Ray it looks like you have a collapsed lung caused by fluid on the lung as a result of pneumonia. To treat it we're going to put you on a strong course of antibiotics and drain your lung," he said.

"Sounds fun!" I replied.

"Don't worry, it's a pretty straight forward simple procedure," he tried to reassure me with a shit eating grin on his face.

I was moved into my own room and put on a drip of antibiotics and hooked up to a monitor which measured my oxygen saturation, blood pressure, and pulse rate.

The lung drain was to be performed the next morning, as that's when the doctor appointed to do the procedure was in next.

I thought it would be good idea to let my family know what's going on, for all they knew I'd got up and gone to work as normal, plus I needed to get my car from the doctor's surgery. So, I texted my sister:

Hey babba I'm in Shrewsbury hospital got a collapsed lung and pneumonia can you get Liam to pick my car up from the surgery oh and tell dad x

She replied with:

OMG WTF are you ok? X

I filled her in on my morning antics.

My sister's boyfriend did the honours and retrieved my car, and my dad, step mum, sister and Aunty Margaret came and visited me in Shrewsbury, which was nice.

I think it took them all by surprise. My sister brought me a stash of sweets to cheer me up, as well as some essentials, like my phone charger, tablet for watching films, and some clothes.

It was nice to catch up with Aunty Margaret, who was really concerned about me.

After I explained to them what happened in detail I tried to tell them all not to worry and that I was fine, which isn't very convincing when you're lying in a hospital bed gasping to breathe.

They eventually left and I was given some codeine to ease the pain enough for me to get some rest for the night.

What a Morning!

I was awake pretty early the next morning, as getting any decent sleep seemed like a distant memory now. I'm up and about an hour and a half before a nurse came to take my observations.

She asked me how I was doing.

"Never better!" I replied, which got a chuckle. I can't help it, I'm that cynical about life, sarcasm is a natural reaction, but if it gets a laugh then it abides by my mantra of making a positive out of a negative situation.

It's about another half hour before a female doctor entered with two colleagues, one male one female, they all held clipboards.

The doctor must have been in her mid 30's average height and very pretty. I remember thinking, "Of course, it's going be a hot doctor to do this procedure on me!"

She introduced her colleagues as student nurses and asked if I minded if they could watch the procedure. I don't think it's every day they have someone in for a lung drain. A lung drain! It just sounds nasty, doesn't it?

Anyway, "The more the merrier," I told her through a forced smile.

I can't remember too much about the two student nurses other than they were in their early 20's and you could tell they were still wet behind the ears as I could sense their excitement when I gave my permission for them to watch.

They stared at me with intrigue, as if I was some rare species.

The hot doctor explained the procedure to me, which basically meant they were going to cut a hole in my side, feed a tube in till it reached the bottom of the well of fluid that had emerged on the outside of my lung, which was the cause of the collapse.

Once the tube was in place it should have drained the fluid into a small clear sealed bucket, like measuring container of 1.5 litres in capacity and about 15cm in diameter.

She finished the talk through of the procedure by mentioning that, in some cases, the tube could catch a vein causing a bleed, in which case the tube would have to be repositioned. I signed the consent form and thought, *well, this is going to be a barrel of laughs, isn't it?*

She asked me to sit up on the side of the bed with my legs hanging over the side and to remove my shirt.

As I'm doing that, she left the room and returned wheeling in a stainless-steel trolley with a flat top covered with all sorts of intimidating items such as the strange looking clear bucket with a handle and long tube protruding from the sealed top of it, a syringe with a big needle, a scalpel, medical dressing, tape and a few other bits and pieces.

The two student nurses are stood behind eagerly waiting for the exhibition to begin.

The hot doc got gloved up and ready for action.

She was behind me to my left side, just out of view, as she's asked me to stay straight and to lean forward slightly as she listened to various spots around my side and back with a stethoscope.

She then began to feel my side to which I winced in pain. I wondered what she's doing when I realised that she was counting my ribs looking for spacing.

She finds the spot she's looking for and keeps three fingers on it as she grabs the syringe with her free hand and brings it towards my side about half-way between my armpit and pelvis.

"Now, I'm just going to give you some anaesthetic to numb the area, you're going to feel a sharp prick and then a warm sensation as the anaesthetic starts to work, ok?" she said as she puts the needle in me, then…

Bingo! Ladies and gentlemen, we have just hit an all time high on the pain threshold!

The pain is that sharp, severe, and sudden that it caught me off guard and I released a "FUCK IT!" and that was just from the needle going in, then all that pain I was feeling got engulfed in flames as she pressed the plunger on the syringe and pushed the anaesthetic into me.

I'm panting short shallow breaths as the doctor massaged the area causing even more pain.

I told her to stop and give me a minute.

My brow was sweating at this point and I was still panting.

She's expected the anaesthetic to have kicked in by now, but it clearly hadn't, so she asked one of the student nurses to get another dose of anaesthetic, which the young man quickly did.

By the time he got back and handed it to the doctor, the effects of the first dose had started to work, marginally. The second dose was painfully administered, and she continued massaging the anaesthetic around my side, though it felt more like she was kneading me than massaging me.

My whole left side was numb, though there was still a pain inside. It was the collapsed lung I could feel it, it was a horrible feeling and hard to describe, because until then I'd never felt my lungs. They were just something I took for granted, working away inside me.

So to have felt one collapse was very strange.

"I'm just going to make an incision so we can insert the tube, Oliver," she said as she made a cut in line with my armpit towards my back which I couldn't feel, due to the numbness of the anaesthetic, or see as it was behind me.

"Now I'm just going put the tube in to the incision and feed it to the cavity where the fluid is building up, you may feel a strange sensation."

She wasn't wrong. I could feel every inch of the tube travelling down my side.

"The liquid that comes out should be clear with a possible red tinge from the initial incision and should be a slow steady flow," she said as the tube was going in.

Then the liquid started coming back out of the tube into the bucket. But it wasn't a clear liquid it was a dark red liquid, and it was coming out fast. So fast, in fact, that it filled 500ml within seconds.

"Oh, it looks like we may have caught a vein," she said, as she pulled the tube back out.

I noticed her tone had shifted from confident to one of concern.

The sensation of the tube sliding back out of me made my stomach lurch and a wave of nausea crashed over me.

When the tube is pulled all the way out, she asked one of the student nurses to hold a patch of dressing on the incision.

The doctor, who didn't seem all that hot to me anymore funnily enough, left with the drain bucket half full of a dark red liquid, which looked too thin to be just blood but still gross none the less.

I'm still sat on the side of the bed, bent forward slightly, trying to compose myself and concentrate on my breathing, all the while thinking, *Well this is going well!*

Moments later, she returned to the room, drain bucket now empty, followed by another doctor, this time male tall dark hair, light skin. Couldn't really see his face, as he already had a face mask on, but the look in his eyes was all business.

He introduced himself to me as he washed his hands and got gloved up.

He didn't acknowledge the two students behind me. He instructed the female doctor to administer me with a drug which I'm not going to pretend to remember the name of, but basically, it's a blood coagulant to slow the bleeding down which she did via a syringe through the cannula in my right arm, from when they hooked me up to have antibiotics intravenously.

A cannula, for those of you that don't know, is a needle with a short tube off it with a connector the other end, the needle goes into a vein and the connector connects to a drip or can be connected to a syringe to administer medication.

As that is happening, the male doctor had taken the now empty drain bucket and positioned himself behind my left side and asked the student nurse holding the patch on the hole in my back to step aside, as he repeated the procedure of first listening to various spots around my back and chest followed by feeling for a certain position on my ribs.

This time it didn't hurt as much due to the numbness of the anaesthetic.

He inserted the tube back into me again, slowly feeding it down my side, which got another turn from my stomach till eventually he stopped.

The room was deadly silent, and I could feel all eyes on me.

Then the liquid started coming back up the tube and down into the bucket. A slow, steady drip of lighter red liquid this time.

"There we go," he said in a calm tone, which gave me a sense of relief. The coagulant must have worked.

He explained to me that I would have to stay in while the lung was being drained and that it will be uncomfortable for the next few days while I've got the drain in. I started coughing, which startled me because the pain was blinding. To which he continued explaining that that was normal because the fluid was being drained, it meant that there was space in the cavity for my lung to re-inflate.

Fun fact! It is more painful for the human lung to re-inflate than it is to collapse!

He finished by telling me that I would get something to manage pain shortly. He then asked the female doctor if she was ok to finish up, to which she agreed and thanked him very much before he signed something on a clipboard and left.

I had a couple of stitches put in where the tube entered me and it was taped to keep in place and I was allowed to put my shirt back, though it was lifted on one side by the tube and bucket which now hung off a hook on the side of the bed.

I lay down but couldn't lay flat as I had a tube protruding out of the side of my back so had to lay with my left side slightly lifted.

After stitching me up and getting me settled, the female doctor apologised for any pain or discomfort she may have caused, to which I reassured her that I was fine and there was no point ruining her day by making her feel guilty that there were complications to the procedure.

I'm not a vindictive person and I think there's enough hate and blame in this world, and if you go through your life blaming people for every bad thing that happens in your life, I think it just makes you bitter and who wants to live life being bitter all the time?

She finished by telling me that someone would be round to take another X-Ray and that the specialist consultant would see me later that afternoon.

The two student nurses had come into view with forced smiles of politeness, but their eyes looked as though they had just witnessed a car crash.

On their way out, they thanked me very much, which I welcomed them, holding back a smirk as I let out a cough and winced.

About five minutes later, a pair of nurses came in wheeling the portable X-Ray machine and we went through the rigmarole of having the X-ray after which I was left to get some rest.

What a fucking morning! I thought.

Breaking News!

I lay on the bed lop sided, being punished with a sharp stabbing pain which accompanied each cough, an hour or so passed when a nurse came in.

She was an older nurse, I would say in her 50's, with dark curly hair and glasses. She picked up my chart to fill in the observations and comes over to the left side of me where the monitors are and where my drain bucket is, and starts filling in the observation sheet, checking the monitor and checking the drain bucket to see how much fluid has come out.

When I tried and stifled a cough and couldn't, I ended up coughing more and groaning in pain.

She grabbed my hand and started patting it softly as I had my coughing fit. "I know, I know," she said. "It will get better, it will get better." She carried on like she was calming a child.

I could tell from the genuine sorrow in her eyes that it was a maternal instinct. I found her concern comforting and it took my mind off the pain briefly, because it made me think about how amazing human nature can be.

I mean, here I was, a complete stranger to this woman, and within minutes she is showing genuine concern for my well being. Now you might say, 'well it's her job to', which I would agree to a certain degree, but not everyone in the healthcare system is like that as I find out later on.

As my coughing fit subsides, she handed me some water and said she would go see someone about some pain relief for me and left the room.

I had been given some codeine and paracetamol, which toned the pain down and made things a little more bearable as long as I wasn't coughing, which was hard not to do.

Lunch time soon came around, which I was glad of because I was ravenous as I missed breakfast due to what felt like having two doctors kick the shit out of me all morning.

It wasn't that bad as it turned out, the hospital food I mean, not the trauma I'd just been through.

Cheese sandwich and some sponge pudding with custard. I thought the sponge and custard was really nice in a comforting way, as simple as it was, it brought me a little bit of joy and reminded me that, all though life throws shit at you, you have no right to be a sob story as there's millions of people out there less fortunate.

I reflected on my current situation.

OK, I've got a collapsed lung and pneumonia, and there were some complications, and I know I've made light of the situation but that's just a coping mechanism. I am very self aware. But what if this happened and I was in another country, which didn't have a national health service, and what if I couldn't afford health insurance for whatever reason?

I'd be dead or certainly on my way.

I suppose the point I'm trying to make is that you have to look at the bigger picture to get a good perspective on something.

The remnants of my devoured lunch was taken away by one of the hospital dinner ladies, but not before I got to choose what I wanted for tea time.

I chose the cottage pie option and I am left to rest again.

It had gone mid afternoon when I got a visit from the respiratory specialist. Gone was the arrogant grin of the day before.

He held a manila file in his hands greets me and asked how I was.

I pressed the controller on the bed to lift me upright and replied, "I've had better days."

He chuckled nervously and said, "I bet you have Mr Morrison, by the sounds of it you've been through the mill a bit."

I replied with, "Well it didn't seem to go **straightforward,** put it that way," with extra emphasis on "straight forward".

He got the point I was making and continued with, "No it didn't. Did you know you have a broken rib?"

I told him I had an idea of one but wasn't certain.

He came closer, opening the manila file, and showed me an X-ray of my chest. "This is the first X-ray we did when you came in yesterday, these are your ribs and this light patch, well, this is the fluid on your lung that we were concerned about."

He turned the X-ray towards me, and I saw what looked to be a negative image. I saw my ribs in white and halfway down them I saw a white blur, which was the fluid.

"Ok," I said, confirming my understanding so far.

He pulled out another X-ray and held it next to the first and said, "Now, this is an X-ray of your chest after we finished the procedure."

I looked at the second X-ray and noticed the faint outline of the drain tube going down the right side of the image till it disappeared into the blurred part. I also saw one of the ribs has a step in it now.

I returned my gaze to the first image to locate the rib in question and notice a faint line in the otherwise straight rib.

"Your rib must have been sitting straight at the time of the first X-ray and we were focused on the fluid on your lung at the time, overlooking the broken rib, which is a clean break by the way. How did you break it?" he asked.

I told him I was just coughing.

"Really? It's not unheard of but it is rare. When you're all fixed up, I will suggest looking into your bone density. Because your rib is broken, you are flexing it apart every time you cough which caused a rupture, which is why there was a lot of blood in the fluid when we initially went in, but you seem to be doing really well now and you are responding well to the treatment. The flow of fluid being drained is slow and steady which is what we want. I can only apologise for the complications that occurred, but rest assured you're going in the right direction now and we'll have you out of here in no time. But in the meantime, we will monitor the fluid being drained and keep you on a course of antibiotics. Just try and get some rest," he explained.

I nodded in agreement and he asked if I had any questions for him which I didn't, so he left.

Well, that explained why I was in so much pain when I was being injected with anaesthetic; a six-inch needle being driven directly into a broken rib will do that.

In hindsight, if the snapped rib had been spotted before the procedure rather than after, things might have gone more smoothly don't you think?

Ha! It could only happen to me, I thought, and positioned the bed back into an almost horizontal position and spent the rest of the afternoon on my phone, updating friends and family on my situation.

That did the trick

Another half hour later and a male nurse entered the room holding a small paper cup, a lot like the ones you get at fast food places to put sauce in from the dispenser. Somehow I didn't think he had a shot of ketchup in there for me.

He introduced himself and asked me if I had any allergies to any medicines.

I told him I didn't, and he handed me the little cup, telling me that he was giving me some morphine.

I looked in the cup and saw an unimpressive tiny yellow pill. *Oh well*, I thought, *bottoms up*, and threw the pill down my throat like a shot of tequila before washing it down with a sip of water.

The male nurse took the paper cup and told me that, as they needed the room, I was to be moved to a ward.

He opened the door and shouted for another nurse to come and help transport my drip, which was on a wheeled stand, while he pushed the bed.

It felt strange as I was pushed out my private room into the hustle and bustle of the hospital corridor.

The place was alive with hospital workers going about their day, from doctors and nurses walking around with files, to cleaners mopping the floor, to patients waiting to be seen.

It was only minutes before I arrived at the ward I would be residing in for the next few days. It was a small ward that held four. I was put on the left of the entrance, furthest way, with two patients opposite me and one next to me on my right.

The chap to my right was a big man who looked to be in his sixties with grey hair. I remember he had big bulging eyes which were red round the edges.

The bloke across from me was the opposite in build, with a skinny frame. He also looked a lot older than me, with dark black and grey hair. He was sitting in an armchair next to his bed facing me with an oxygen mask on, looking like he was having difficulty breathing as he had a constant wheeze.

I couldn't see the third gentleman properly as he was sleeping on his side with his back to me.

My eyes fell to half mast, and I noticed I wasn't coughing anymore. What a relief- the pain wasn't aggravating me any more.

It's not long before I realised I'm not in any pain at all. In fact, *I'm pretty high. Nope, I'm really high.*

I had a little chuckle to myself thinking, *Ha! Friday night and I'm off my nut who'd have thought,* and passed out.

Sleeping Beauty & the Beast

I think now would be a good idea to tell you all about a little condition I have called obstructive sleep apnoea, which means that I stop breathing in my sleep due to my throat relaxing so much it causes an obstruction to my airways, thus Obstructive Sleep Apnoea.

The body is an amazing instrument even when it's unconscious it will do what it needs to do to survive. My body will detect that I have stopped breathing and eventually I'll take a big gasp of breath, forcing air through the closed throat, making an all-mighty snoring sound, not too dissimilar, I would think, to the sound of a bear fucking a gorilla.

So, although I might be asleep, the beast is roaring. It's a condition I've had since I was a child with everyone thinking that I was just a loud snorer, but as I got older, I knew it was something more than that.

Because I've had it from a young age it is something natural to me, though I have frightened the life out of previous girlfriends over the years, especially during the beginning stages of the relationship.

Waking up to someone who was petrified you'd died over and over throughout the night is a hard start to any relationship. And before you say it, yes, I have looked into treatment for it.

The treatment for sleep apnoea is not as medically advanced as it could be. There's only one treatment that the NHS offer and that's called the CPAP machine.

Cpap stands for Continuous Positive Airways Pressure, which basically is a tight mask that goes on your face, strapped around your head, which continuously pumps air into your mouth and nose forcing it down your airways.

Remember those times as a kid, when you used to stick your head out of the car window going down the motorway? Well, that's what it feels like when you're wearing one of those contraptions, so you can imagine how difficult it is to sleep with one on.

There are different types of sleep apnoea; so, you can't tell me that one form of treatment is suitable for all cases. I have obstructive sleep apnoea. How about dealing with the obstruction, say, via a corrective operation?

Well, that's my argument, anyway, and is ongoing with the sleep clinic. Anyway, you can imagine the fun and games I had with it at Shrewsbury hospital with the night nurses, as that was my first night I actually fell asleep properly, as the morphine had worked, meaning the pain was alleviated and I was exhausted from the procedure.

It was an ungodly hour of the night/morning when I was rudely awaken by a gentle shaking of my shoulder and a beeping noise as I slowly regained consciousness.

My eyes still shut, the beeping noise stopped and is replaced by my name?

"Oliver...Oliver, love...Oliver, are you ok?"

I slowly opened my eyes to a female nurse gently shaking me.

"Oliver are you ok?" she said.

Well, I would be if you'd stop shaking me, I thought, confused by the whole situation and the fact that I was exhausted and still under the influence of the morphine.

I replied with a croaked voice from a dry throat, "Yeah, I'm fine. Why? What's going on?"

She handed me a glass of water with a look of grave concern and said, "Oliver, your oxygen saturation levels were down to 60%! But they've seemed to have gone back up now."

Shit, I thought. *They don't know about my sleep apnoea.*

I explained to the nurse my condition and that I'd had it since a kid. She was shocked at the severity of it.

"Would you like me to get you a cpap machine?" she asked.

"No thank you I have tried using them many times before and I can't sleep with them on making it counterproductive." I replied

"Well we'll have to keep a close eye on you because it's dangerous for your health if your oxygen saturation levels drop by that much." She said.

I tried to reassure them that I wouldn't pop my clogs on them if they just let me sleep. But, sure enough, as soon as I fell into a deep sleep, the monitor would start beeping and I would get woken up by an overly concerned nurse.

Morning came around, and after what felt like a round of Chinese sleep deprivation torture, I realised my bladder was full. Great!

I got out of bed, wheeling my drip stand with one hand and carrying my bucket of badness with the other hand. The toilet room was in the same ward and only about 20 feet from my bed, but it was still a mission to accomplish unaided, which I managed to do, and it gave me a sense of achievement.

It's the little victories in life that make all the difference, I thought.

Breakfast was served. Cereal, toast, and apple juice is on the menu that day, which wasn't bad. The night shift of nurses swapped over to the day shift and my sleep apnoea was reported to the day shift, because when the specialist came round to see me, just after lunch, it was mentioned amongst other things such as me having to stay in for the rest of the weekend, as my drain bucket had filled another 500ml of fluid which is emptied.

It was nothing to worry about, though, he just wanted to make sure as much of the fluid was drained as possible.

He asked me about my sleep apnoea which I explained to him in detail and that I've had it since a kid.

He noted that it is an issue that's ongoing with the sleep clinic, and if I was happy sleeping unaided, that they would lower the threshold of the oxygen saturation monitor and let me sleep through the night.

It's important that I got rest to be able to heal and that he'd be changing my pain relief to paracetamol and oral morph, which is a liquid morphine, meaning the dosage can be monitored better, and it isn't as heavy as the tablet. In other words, it wouldn't knock me for six.

I'd finally be able to get some good rest but was gutted about having to stay the weekend.

The specialist left and I dozed off for about an hour before getting a welcome visit from my aunt who brought me some obligatory grapes- oh the cliché!

I insisted I didn't want my family to bother visiting me as I couldn't do anything, plus, I didn't want to put anybody out as it was a half hour journey each way for everyone at home.

My aunt lived in Shrewsbury so it was only five minutes from her. I filled her in on the procedure and the restless night of sleep, which shocked her to say the least.

"Oh god kidda, you have been through it haven't you!"

We chatted some more before visiting time was over.

It wasn't long after the last meal of the day when a pair of young trainee doctors approached me, both female, one of Asian mixed race with light brown skin with long dark hair and a plain accent, and the other with a pale complexion and long ginger hair with an Irish accent, both in their early 20's max.

They introduced themselves and told me that they had heard about my case and wondered if I minded going through what happened to me over the last couple of days.

Why not? I thought, I've got nothing else to do.

They draw the privacy curtain around my bed as I began to recount the previous day's event.

I remember telling them everything that had happened to me as they sat at my bedside furiously writing notes on their pads.

It looked like they are studying some zoo animal.

When I finished telling them what happened, they stood up, shook my hand, thanked me with big smiles as if I'd given them some research gold, then they drew the curtains back and left.

After they left, I laid in bed with the telly on.

The news was on, and there's a report of a strange virus in china, which originated in a seafood market in Wuhan, has confirmed human to human transmission and has already started to claim lives. The symptom of the virus is similar to flu and pneumonia and attacks the respiratory system.

Hmmm? That sounds familiar, I thought and changed the channel to something mind numbing, just to have on in the background.

I was tired and had a lot of pain killers running through my system at the time so never gave it a second thought. It wasn't long before I eventually passed out and fell asleep.

Breathe!

I woke up pretty early due to the morphine wearing off. It was about 6 in the morning.

I laid there with my eyes still shut, as my old friend pain starts to awaken with me.

I notice that I was actually lying flat on my back; I was lying on the drain tube - *Shit!*

I leaned over on to my right side, where I was greeted by the big chap in the bed next to me, laying on his side facing me. He was staring at me; actually, with his big bulging eyes that made his stare even more intense.

I was caught off guard by the whole situation, plus the pain was getting more agitating now, so I just nodded a "Morning" to him, to which he replied, in a slight Birmingham accent, "You got to sort that sleeping out kidda, It's no good for you. I was frighten to death! You stop breathing!"

"I know, I know, but it's something I've had nearly all my life, so don't worry about it, I'm fine really," I said.

He carried on with, "You had me worried kidda. I've been up all night willing you to breathe every time you stop. Breathe! I've been going, just breathe!'"

I chuckled and reassured him I was fine. He told me his name was Les and then I introduced myself, and it turns out he suffered from sleep apnoea as well but was a custom to using the cpap machine. We chatted until breakfast, he was actually a nice old chap.

A nurse came round mid morning with more painkillers, to my relief, but to also check my drain bucket, which was about three quarters full of quite a dark red liquid, from when I'd laid on my back.

I must have caused it to bleed again.

The nurse lifted the bucket to look at it and took a sharp breath in, making the noise a mechanic makes just before he tells you it's going to be an expensive job.

"There's still a bit of fluid coming out of you isn't there," she said as she disconnects the bucket from the tube and leaves to empty the bucket.

She returned with the empty bucket, reconnected it and said, "We're definitely keeping you for the weekend."

"Oh joy," I replied.

"We're not that bad, are we?"

I flushed with embarrassment, *Shit, I didn't mean to offend her.* "I didn't mean it like," I said, stumbling on my words, before she laughed at me and walked off to change my drinking water.

After she left, I lay there, propped to one side as not to lie on my drain tube, on my phone filling in my friends and family on my current situation.

My friends thought the whole ordeal was crazy and couldn't believe it. I thought it was crazy and couldn't believe it half the time, then I realise it's typical of me.

I don't get to just have a cold or flu, be ill for a week, and get over it. Oh no. Life has a different plan for me and has to do it in spectacular fashion with a snapped rib, pneumonia, and collapsed lung.

Still, I can't let it get me down. I won't let it get me down.

I went through the motions of the day, stared at the TV, ate, took pain killers and antibiotics, which were now swapped from IV to oral, then tried to get some sleep for the night.

The next day the drain bucket was only a quarter full, and the liquid was a light colour, so it looked promising for me to go home at the end of the weekend as suggested.

Home Sweet Home

One...Two...Three!

Monday finally came around and it was mid morning before the specialist came to see me accompanied by a nurse.

He inspected the drain bucket and was satisfied enough so instructed the nurse to take it away.

The nurse disconnected the tube from the bucket and left with it.

"So how are you feeling" he asked.

"Well I'm still in a lot of pain which gets worse with every cough I have, which seems to be regular" I said

"The cough is natural for someone whose lung has collapsed, as it is just the lung healing and that it's just unfortunate that you have a broken rib as well. The cough will go with time. As for the rib, that will have to heal on its own there really isn't anything we can do for that apart from manage the pain" he explained.

He advised a course of Paracetamol and codeine and at 2 weeks off work.

By this time, the nurse had returned, he asked her to sort out the tube protruding from my back as he went off to get my medication and sort out my discharge letter.

The nurse gloved up and closed the privacy curtain; *Oh shit,* I thought, *this is not going to be nice.*

The nurse asked me to sit on the side of the bed with my legs over the side and to take my top off. She held the tube in one hand and pushed against the entry wound of the tube with the other hand.

"Now, I want you to take a deep breath in on the count of three," she said. I nodded in agreement. "One...........Two......"

Oh fuck, I thought.

"Three!" she said as she pulled on the tube which has been inside me for the last three days.

I took a deep breath in as she did it and my stomach flips a 180, nearly presenting my breakfast, but it was all over in an instant, thank god.

She stitched up the hole with two stitches that would dissolve on their own in about a week and left.

I texted my sister and asked her to come and get me while I waited for the paperwork to be completed.

After about ten minutes, I was presented with a bag of medication and my discharge letter by the specialist who informed me that I'd be getting a follow up appointment in about four weeks' time. I thanked him for all his help, and he sent me on my way.

It's not long before my sister arrived to collect me. I remember waiting for her outside the Hospital and reflecting on the whole experience and thinking, *What the fuck was that all about?!*

I gave my sister an update on the journey home. When I eventually got home my dad and step mum were there to greet me.

"All fixed up now?" my dad asked half mocking, half enquiring.

"To a fashion, but got a long way to go yet, though," I said as I headed up to my room.

"Oh right," he replied, not knowing what else to say.

He meant well, but I just hadn't got the energy to explain the whole recovery process to him. He's in his seventies and has spent most of his working life on an oil rig or ship. He'd be away months at a time as I was growing up for most of mine and my siblings lives. He's an incredibly intelligent man, being a geophysicist by trade, but there's an absence of people skills and how to handle people situations.

Whereas I'm the complete opposite. I love people, I love spending time with my friends and family. I love helping people with whatever issues they may have. At one point in time, I was considered as a figure of council to many of my friends who would come speak to me if they had a problem and I'd mainly just listen and give them my perspective of the situation, which is sometimes all somebody needs to get through something; an outside perspective.

Now, it was entirely up to that person if they took on board my views or not, but even just the act of giving someone the time to listen to their problems can help.

I suppose, what I'm trying to say, is that my dad and I are worlds apart.

I got changed into some fresh, comfy clothes and got into bed, then the coughing started, shooting pain straight to my rib. I had to lay flat on my back too, because if I lent slightly to one side or the other, it sent a pain to my broken rib.

Least I'm home, I thought.

The next morning I was exhausted from a night of disturbed sleep due to the stabbing pain in my rib every time I moved or coughed. I only made it as far as the bottom of the stairs before having another coughing fit.

My step mum came downstairs and ushered me up to my room and got a drink for me.

"Jeeze, sounds like you should still be in hospital," my dad said from the top of the stairs.

"It's my lung recovering, it's not going to happen overnight!" I snapped at him as I pass.

Shit! I instantly felt guilty for shouting at him, but it was a reflex from the shear amount of pain I was in.

I laid back in an upright position on my bed, grabbed my phone and made an appointment with my doctors thinking *I've been to my doctors more times in this last week than I have in the last decade!* The pain was getting unbearable.

My step mum drove me to my doctor surgery later that day for my appointment. It's not my regular doctor again as it's an emergency appointment.

As I walked into the doctor's office he sat at his desk, intently looking at his computer screen, without looking up he tells me to come in and take a seat.

I couldn't place his accent, but it put me at ease for some reason. It was Australian or Kiwi, but very slight.

I took a seat as he finished reading whatever he was reading on his screen and he began with, "Crikey, you've had a rough time, haven't you?"

Australian! I immediately thought he's got to be an Aussie. "You could say that," I replied.

"What can I do for you?" he asked, so I told him about the pain I was in and that the hospital gave me codeine and two weeks rest.

He let out a short laugh of optimism and said, "Well, if you were on morphine in the hospital to manage the pain, why on earth did they think that codeine would manage it out of hospital?" He shook his head in disbelief. "Right, I'm going to prescribe you with oral morph as long as you don't go selling it on the streets," he joked, "and I'm going to write you a sick note for 6 weeks, and if you're still feeling like you need more time to heal, you come back and see me," he finished.

Wow! I thought *someone with a bit a sense at last!* I collected my prescription and went home.

The Road to Recovery

With some proper painkillers I was able to begin my journey down the long road to recovery.

The broken rib was the main issue, every movement I made hurt and as for the coughing fits, well, that just ramped up the pain tenfold.

I would only use the morphine at night to help me sleep. I would be getting in two to three-hour segments, as that was how long the morphine would last before the pain would creep back in.

I didn't use it in the day as I didn't want to become dependent on it, a morphine addiction was the last thing I needed.

I definitely wasn't going to be doing cartwheels any time soon, I'd have a coughing fit just from going down the stairs for a drink or food.

Sometime that week there were reports of the first case of Covid-19 in the U.K. Covid-19 was the name of the strange flu-like virus which originated from the fishing market in Wuhan, China.

The reports were all over the media saying that it had spread out of the China province to Thailand and the U.S with around 500 cases and 17 deaths.

That's absolutely nuts, I thought.

The more I heard about it, the more it convinced me that I must have had this so-called deadly flu. I mean, it's not every day you have a cough so bad you snap one of your own ribs. I remind myself to bring it up with the specialist at my next appointment in about four weeks' time.

A couple of weeks passed and I was able to get about the house without too much difficulty. I was still having coughing fits, but they were getting further apart. There was a lump on my left side where my rib had set crooked. I was still using the morphine at night, but had lowered the dose because I started getting itchy palms and cold sweats, which freaked me out because I was afraid I was beginning to look like a cast member of Train spotting.

There's now 9 confirmed cases in the U.K of this deadly virus from China. Other countries with confirmed cases included Germany, Hong Kong, Singapore, South Korea, Malaysia and more.

China was on a national lockdown which I think was crazy.

So, this virus seems to attack the respiratory system and is potentially dangerous, especially if you're older and have underlying health problems, but there is a survival rate of over 99% and governments are locking down whole countries because of it? Something seemed fishy to me.

Another couple of weeks passed and I was feeling a lot better; getting stronger by the day. Still having coughing fits but not very often. If I went out for a brisk walk it would be a bit too much for me, I'll start coughing rather than get out of breath, but I was getting there.

I went back to the hospital for a follow up appointment which went pretty straight forward.

"How is your recovery progressing" The specialist asked.

"It's going ok I suppose, I'm still having the odd coughing fit but the fits are getting further apart, I can feel a lump in my side where my ribs healed crooked" I told him.

"Well the cough is natural and will go in time, Unfortunately there is nothing we can do for your rib but it does remind me, we must get you a bone density scan organised" he replied

"Ok, before I go though do you think it is a possibility that the illness that caused all this for me was the Covid-19 virus?" I asked him.

"No it couldn't have been it wasn't in the country when you first came down with the illness" he replied nonchalantly.

I should have pressed him on the subject but what difference did it make? I left the hospital and headed home thinking about what the specialist said about the Covid-19 virus not being in the U.K when I was ill.

The virus originated in China at the end of 2019, the first **reported** case in the U.K was January 23, 2020. I was ill and in hospital only a week before. So, are we to take as gospel truth, that the Covid-19 virus was not in this country any time before January 23?

Just because that's when the first **reported** case was?

Hmmm....it made me suspicious of how the media were handling the whole situation.

WTF?

It was the middle of March when I returned to work, but only for a couple of days a week, to phase me back into work.

I have been with the company for about 7 years now and we're a tight knit group. I look after the parts department for the company, as well as some sales work when needed.

It can be pretty stressful in the summer when it's peak season and our workshop is full, customers can be so impatient. The irony is that we could have a professional mower in from a golf course having an extensive amount of work doing to it, which would take us weeks to do and cost the club money in down time, without any hassle, yet Mrs Jones, down the road, who has her little walk behind mower in for repair is on the phone tearing me a new asshole because she's having to wait few extra days because we have to wait for parts to come in!

I mean, how blessed must you be if all you have in life to be angry about is the length of time someone is taking to fix your mower.

"Oh, that can't happen very often," I hear you say. Yeah, it can and yes it does, all summer, in fact, but I think one of the reasons I've got on so well at my work is that I don't let it get to me.

I often think to myself *You can't, you've just got to accept that there are obnoxious people out there and I for one will not give them the satisfaction of getting me down,* but I suppose that has come with experience.

When I first started, I used to think, *Fuck! Why are people so horrible? What could I have done to prevent that from happening?"* But I learnt quite quickly that it is what it is and that you are not going to please all the people all the time, just some of the people some of the time.

It was good to be back at work. Everyone there had been concerned about me and what I'd been through.

I was only back at work about a week and half when it happened. On March 23rd, 2020, due to the threat of the Covid-19 virus, the Prime Minister announced a national lockdown, meaning everyone was to stay in their homes, only essential businesses are to remain trading, such as the food industry and related businesses such as supermarkets and convenience stores.

All non-essential businesses were to close with immediate effect, such as pubs and restaurants, gyms, and hairdressers.

Those being told to stay at home would be eligible to a furlough scheme which meant the government were going to pay 80% of your wage to stay at home.......*What the fuck!*

Everyone at my work got the same text that night from our boss telling us that we were to stay home as instructed by the government.

With the business supporting the farm industry it technically meant that the business was essential and because my boss, his wife and son all lived under one roof, they were able to work together, while the rest of the company were furloughed.

I never thought I would ever be witness to a global pandemic in my lifetime.

By April, the average amount of deaths in the U.K were about 800 a day and the number of worldwide cases passed a million.

Lockdown

The novelty of not being at work wore off fast. The only form of social connection I had was a video game *Call of Duty*, where I could communicate via headset in a party of six.

To be honest, I was very grateful for this as it meant I could stay in touch with my brother who lives in Scotland, as well as some of my other mates. There were many times when we would use the game just as a platform to have a social meeting rather than actually playing the game.

Meanwhile, hospitals all over the country were struggling due to the sheer volume of patients with the Covid-19 virus, which had caused a global pandemic.

The prime minister himself came down with the virus and had to go to intensive care but recovered and was discharged from hospital a couple of weeks later, as the number of cases worldwide passed 2 million.

The Economist Intelligence Unit announced the world economy may face a double recession.

The number of confirmed cases in the U.S.A reached 700,000, hospitals in Japan were on the brink of collapse, and NHS bosses asked doctors and nurses to work without PPE because of a shortage.

The world seemed like it was going into chaos, and it was only a couple of months into the pandemic.

The month of May came around and the madness continued. Brazil surpassed 100,000 Covid-19 cases, global Covid-19 death toll passed 250,000, doctors at a Paris hospital in France report evidence that a patient had Covid-19 as early as December 19, a month before the first reported case.

Now that fact was interesting, wasn't it?

Meanwhile, back in sunny Oswestry, everybody was still in lockdown, which means no one was to leave their homes unless they were an essential worker. You were allowed out for 15 minutes a day to walk with a pet or by yourself only, though the 15-minute rule was relaxed by May, but you still weren't allowed to see anyone who wasn't from your household.

My dog got pretty fit during lockdown as there wasn't a lot to do except walk her, and that was my only bit of freedom. I felt sorry for people who lived in the cities where they couldn't just pop out for a walk in the country, who were stuck in a flat or house 24/7.

It was becoming apparent that the lockdown was having a damaging effect on people's mental health.

It's not long before the nation was allowed to meet up in a bubble of 6 people, but they had to be from only 2 households, and they had to be outside. Apparently, this virus finds it easier to get you when you're inside.

Oh, you're also allowed to go to work, but you are urged to stay at home and don't go out, but work from home if you can.

It was all becoming a little confusing and the government weren't looking as though they had a handle on things, as they were changing the rules every five minutes.

It wasn't much longer before June 6th was upon us.

What's the relevance of this date you may ask? Well, it was the day I turned 40! I never thought I would be in the middle of a global pandemic for my 40th and to be honest with you there was a point where I thought I wouldn't make it to 40!

Some friends of mine, who live less than 10 minutes from me in a lovely cottage out in the country, offered to host a private party for a select few of my nearest and dearest.

Now, I know it was against lock down rules, but I didn't force anyone to come, plus with what I'd already been through earlier that year, I felt I was lucky to have made it to 40!

Anyway, a good time was had by all and thanks to the generosity of my amazing mates, I actually came home with a lot more alcohol than I went with, and that was after trying to drink what felt like my own body weight in rum.

It wasn't the 40th I was expecting, but it was a celebration that I hold close to my heart because, although the world was in turmoil, we still pulled together to make the best out of a bad situation, and for my friends to do that for me felt quite special. The hangover also made sure I would never forget that night too.

After the party, it was back to lockdown life, the days turned to weeks and the weeks to months. A lot of places started opening for business but with restrictions.

Just as we thought things were getting better the Prime Minister announced a second national lockdown, meaning all pubs and restaurants closed as well as non-essential shops, leisure, and entertainment venues.

Schools, colleges, and universities were to stay open this time, no households were to mix or meet in private gardens, and everyone was to stay at home, unless it was to go to work or to education.

It's getting sneaky this virus, as going by the governments new lock down rules, the virus can get you if you're at a pub or restaurant, or generally having a good time, but it can't get you at work. Oh, and it's not academic as it turned out.

It was November by the time I'm back at work, only part time though, as me and my colleague had to stagger our shifts so there were no more than 2 people in the office at a time, this was just one of the many new guidelines brought out by the government due to the virus.

The Nightmare's Just Begun

Friday the 13th

Now, my story could have ended there. A snapped rib, collapsed lung, pneumonia, and a pandemic seems enough to go through in a year, doesn't it?

" Oh no. I think not", the universe said.

In fact, that was just a mere warm up, and life being the bitch she can sometimes be, went, "you haven't seen nothing yet, hold my beer!"

Nothing could have prepared me for the events that I am about to tell you.

I can honestly say it is one of the most harrowing experiences I have ever been through.

None the less, I feel it is important to share it.

If not only for your entertainment but to inspire others who are going through a similar experience to not give up and to keep fighting even when you think your chips are down.

It was November 13th, 2020, and ironically enough it was a Friday. I remember I had booked it off work with the following Monday because the new *Call of Duty* game had come out and I planned to spend a long weekend playing it.

Yeah, ok, I know I'm 40 and it's only a video game but we were in the middle of a pandemic so don't judge me!

Anyway, as it happened, I didn't end up playing the game on the Friday.

It was nearly midnight, and I was in bed watching a film. It was the Korean film Parasite. I'd wanted to watch it for a while because it won an Oscar for best film plus some other awards.

I was enjoying the film until I felt a buzzing sensation start at the base of my neck and around the back of my head and within a matter of seconds there was darkness, just darkness.

It was about ten minutes before I started regaining consciousness; I sat up on the side of the bed, head still buzzing, then stood up. As I stood, I realised my eyes were still closed and my head was facing down, as if my neck muscle had failed, and I couldn't lift it.

Oh, fuck this isn't good, I thought and just sat back down head still limp. *Breathe, just breathe.*

A few seconds later, my consciousness caught up with me. My eyes opened and I lifted my head. The buzzing sensation had been replaced with a searing pain at the base of my neck followed by a thumping pain in my head which was getting worse by the second.

A sudden wave of nausea came over me making me feel sick, so I stumbled to the bathroom to throw up.

Once I'd emptied my stomach, the nausea subsided but the blinding headache was still present.

I returned to my room and took some painkillers and tried to get some sleep.

The next day was no better, in fact it, was worse. It felt like someone was trying to break out of my head with a sledgehammer.

A continuous, torturous thumping inside my head accompanied by a sharp stabbing pain in the base of my neck.

Because it was Saturday, I knew my doctor's surgery wouldn't be open till Monday, so I thought the best plan of action was to ride it out till then, and see what they suggest, so I took more painkillers and tried to rest as much as I could.

By now I was taking a cocktail of Paracetamol, Ibuprofen, and Aspirin; none of which remotely worked as far as pain management goes. In fact, every time I tried to lie flat, my head would start thumping even harder, building pressure with each thump which was in time with my heart.

It would build up so much that the force of it would make me shoot upright in bed into a sitting position as the pain was unbearable.

On Monday there was no sign of this behemoth of a headache going away, although the neck pain was easing off, so I called my doctors surgery.

Because of the pandemic, going to see your doctor wasn't straightforward.

There was an automated message telling me that I was in a queue and that if I was suffering with any symptoms of Coronavirus not to come to the surgery and to call 999 if I'm having trouble breathing or I feel there may be a problem with my heart.

I eventually got to speak to the receptionist who told me that, due to the pandemic, they have been dealing with a high number of patients. Now they were not seeing anyone at the surgery unless it was urgent, but firstly all patients had to have a consultation with a doctor via telephone.

Great, I thought.

She preceded to tell me that the next telephone appointment available was in two days on Wednesday.

Fuck. "I'll take it," I told the receptionist who booked me in to be called by a doctor.

Throwing the towel in

The thumping and pounding continued to get worse. I'd told my dad about it, who didn't think it was that serious, mainly because I was in too much pain to explain to him how bad it was. He just suggested I take some Aspirin, which I already did.

By Tuesday, I think I accidentally overdosed on pain killers as I ended up throwing up a load of them. My head was in such a state I hadn't kept track of how many I'd been taking, plus I wasn't eating very much as I didn't have an appetite. I was just in a world of hurt.

I was sensitive to the light now and had to stay in my bedroom with blinds shut.

Wednesday came and I got my call from my doctor. I explained to him what had happened to me the Friday night and told him the symptoms I was suffering with and he told me that if I was feeling that bad then I should call 111 which is an emergency number set up by the NHS.

Shit! If I have to go to hospital, it's going to be carnage with the whole pandemic situation.

I rode out the pain for another night before admitting defeat and throwing the towel in. I called 111.

After telling them what I'd gone through since Friday, they told me to get to Wrexham Hospital as soon as possible and that they would call ahead to let them know I was coming.

Oh, fuck, they sounded serious. I best do what they say.

It was about 7:30am in the morning when I made the call. As soon as I hung up, I woke my step mum to give me a lift to the hospital.

We all got ready; I made sure to bring my phone charger and charging bank, as I knew that it wasn't going to be a five-minute visit. My step mum drove me to the hospital and my dad came along for the ride, too.

They literally had to just drop me off at the hospital because of Covid restrictions visitors were prohibited.

As I waved goodbye to them, I had no idea that it was very nearly the last time I would see them.

When I walked into the Hospital, the first thing I noticed was how quiet it was.

The way the media was covering the pandemic, I was expecting a skirmish of doctors and nurses battling a hoard of zombies; but it wasn't so.

I got to the reception and told them I had been advised to come here by 111.

After asking for my name and date of birth I was asked to sit and wait in the waiting area.

Here we go, I expected to be sitting around waiting most the day now. I sat in a not very full waiting room, with do not sit signs on every other seat, but it was only about five minutes before my name was called out by a nurse who led me to the triage room, well, it was a ward with various partitions.

I was asked to sit on a bed as she closed the curtains around our partition, she then asked me what was wrong, so I explained to her what had happened since the previous Friday which she noted on a form on a clip board.

When I was done explaining about the sledgehammers trying to break out my head, I had to have a Covid test, which consists of two swabs, one so far down my throat it made me gag and another right up my nostril far enough to bring a tear to my eye.

After violating my face with overgrown ear buds, the nurse kindly left.

As I sat there the pounding in my head got worse. *Fuck. I hope it's nothing serious,* I thought. It wasn't long before a doctor turned up. He introduced himself and asked me what the problem was.

For fuck's sake, can't you just read my file? I thought.

After spending another five minutes recounting what can only be described as the worst Friday the 13th ever, he told me that he would start with various blood test.

He put a canula in my right arm with about three tubes coming off it with connectors. He filled four blood bottles up from the connected canula all with different colour lids.

Christ, leave me some blood.

"Right, we'll get this tested and take it from there, here's something for the pain," the doc said as he handed me some Paracetamol.

"Thanks," I said stifling a laugh at his optimism of the power of paracetamol as he left with my blood samples.

It was just me and the sledgehammers trying to work their way out of my head for what felt like an hour before the doctor returned.

He told me that there were no findings with the initial blood tests, but they are looking further into the bloods. He then told me that he wanted me to have a CT scan, I nodded in agreement.

I couldn't hide the pain by this point, as I was constantly wincing and, as if he read my mind which wouldn't have been hard from the faces I was pulling, the doctor said he was going to give me 1 millilitre of diluted morphine for the pain.

The morphine was given to me with a syringe connected to the canula in my arm.

As soon as he pushed the plunger down, the effects were almost instant, the pounding pain in my head dialled right down to a quiet beating of drums in the distance.

The relief was almost euphoric.

For nearly 6 days my head had felt like it was splitting open, the agony was relentless, from that to virtually no pain at all felt like I'd been reborn.

After he administered the morphine, the doctor led me to the CT department where he handed me over to the CT scan staff who talked me through the scan procedure which was pretty straightforward.

I had to lie still on the scan table while the table moved me in to a big round vessel like contraption which was the scanner itself and took about 15 minutes to complete.

With the scan completed I was led back to the triage area where I waited for the results.

The results came back as clear. *Fuck! What the hell is wrong with me?* I thought, the drumming in my head was starting to get louder.

Oh, shit it's coming back.

The doctor suggests I have lumbar puncture and asked me my thoughts on it.

I must admit, I didn't feel like jumping for joy at the idea, but if it helped get to the bottom of the problem then *crack on*, I thought.

The doctor told me that he would be handing me over to someone else to do the lumbar puncture, so he led me to a room on A & E because they were short on beds.

The room was more like a pod, which they had all over A & E to try and stop the spread of Covid. Each pod had a bed and a monitor in it, with just enough room each side of the bed for you to get round.

As I sat on the bed, the drumming was getting louder, and the monitor was on but not connected to anything so was just beeping constantly.

Beep beep bang bang beep beep bang bang.

Between the beeping of the monitor and the banging in my head it was torture.

The atmosphere in the hospital had changed now I was in A & E. It was busier and everyone was rushing round like blue ass flies.

Three people entered the pod: an older male doctor, a younger male trainee doctor, and a female assistant nurse. The older male doctor introduced himself and his colleagues and explained that they will be performing the lumbar puncture, which involves driving a big needle into the base of your spine and extracting the brain fluid that circulates your brain and runs down your spine.

He also explained the risks involved, but al I heard was "Blah blah blah blah could result in paralysis".

Awesome, let's do it, and I signed the consent form.

The older doctor discussed with the younger hot shot rookie whether he felt he could do the procedure. Hot shot rookie oozed confidence in his answer.

Just then, there was a knock at the door and another nurse asked to speak to the older doctor outside.

I couldn't hear what was said between the two, but it must have been important because the nurse led the doctor away.

Meanwhile, hot shot rookie thought it would be a great opportunity to play Billy big balls in front of his female colleague and proceeded with the lumbar puncture.

He asked me to sit on the side of the bed and lean forward and to lift my shirt as he applied rubbing alcohol to the base of my spine. "You're just going to feel a bit of a sting, but please remember to stay as still as possible till I've removed the needle," he said as he began to drive the needle into my spine.

I draw a sharp breath in as the needle entered me and started going deeper and deeper.

Fuck it stung, and the fucking things going to start coming out of my stomach if he pushes it in any further! Just as I thought that he started retracting the needle till I heard an "All done!" and it was all over.

He taped some cotton wool to the base of my spine and told me to lie back.

He explained that because fluid has been taken from my brain, I would have to lay back to level the fluid out as it's replenishing, and that the procedure can cause a headache as a result.

Great! A headache on top of my headache is just what the doctor ordered as it turns out. *Fuck my life,* I thought.

The older doctor returned as the rookie was finishing up. As they were leaving, I heard him say "oh you've done it, how did it go?"

The rookie nodded with a big grin of achievement, "yes, no problem," he answered as they all left the pod.

I couldn't hear what was said outside the door, but there was a lot of nodding back and forth, then they were on their way.

Alone again in my little pod, the thumping in my head had returned more vicious than ever. Boom Boom.

The pressure was building again, and I had to sit up before my head exploded, then I noticed it again. Beep beep.

Fuck's sake, that fucking monitor's still going!

Boom boom, beep beep, my little pod has become a torture room.

Beep beep, boom boom. *I can't take much more of the pain* I thought.

I was writhing around, holding my head nearly in tears at this point. "Nurse!" I shouted at the door, "Nurse!"

My cries were answered, and a young female nurse came in.

"What's the matter?" she asked.

"I'm in agony here, my heads pounding" I told her.

She looked at my chart and told me she would get someone who can help and leaves. Minutes later, another nurse entered.

At last! I thought, but she had only come in to take an attachment off the monitor that she needed.

"What about my pain relief?" I asked her.

"You what, luvvy?" she replied.

"What about my pain my pain relief?" I repeated.

"Oh, I'm not dealing with you. I've just come for this," she replied as she held up some wires.

As she leaves the room, she held the door open with one hand and shouted, "Is anyone dealing with this gentleman in here?"

Someone replied but I couldn't make out what they were saying so the conversation was one sided.

"I don't know" .... "He wants some pain relief," she continued, all the while I'm thinking, *I can hear you, you know!* And then she just leaves.

Great, I thought.

Beep beep sounded off again followed by the boom boom in my head as I carried on squirming in pain with my head clamped in my hands.

A few minutes later a doctor came in. He must have been late 20's early 30's, slim build with a bald shaved head. He looked at my chart and then at me and I could see the genuine concern in his eyes which resembled fear almost. "My names Andy, I'm the A&E doctor," he began as I continued to writhe around in pain.

"I just want something for the pain," I told him.

"I know, mate, but first I'm going to need you to lie back and be as still as you can," he said with the same amount of caution and intensity of someone dealing with a bomb.

Why is this guy so intense? I thought, then it dawned on me – shit, the lumbar puncture. I tried to lie back and settle.

"Don't worry, I'm going to give you something for the pain, but with what you have just had done to you," he's referring to the lumbar puncture, "You need to lie back and not move about so much, as it can be dangerous for you," he said as he started to fill a syringe with a clear liquid. "You need to keep on at the nurses if you need pain relief, they have a duty of care for you. I'm just doing you a solid, you're not even my patient but I can see the pain and distress you're in, so I'm going to help you, but you must lie back ok?"

I could tell he wasn't impressed with how I'd been treated by the nurses when he said that. Once he had filled the syringe, he began to couple it to the canula in my arm.

I said, "Thank you. The doctor earlier gave me 1ml of morphine diluted before and that seemed to do the trick."

He smirked at me and said, "Mate, I'm giving you 10ml of pure morphine. You're not going to be feeling any pain! Welcome to dragon land!" he said making a whoop noise as he pressed the plunger of the syringe down.

The effects were instant; My eyes shut halfway, and my head fell back against the bed.

"Now I will put on your chart what I've given you and tell whoever is dealing with you, all I want you to do now is just lay back and rest ok?" he said.

I just nodded and tried telling him about the monitor beeping, but I was nearly out of it now, "Can you ugh can you can..." I managed to get out before just sticking my thumb back in the direction of the beeping monitor.

He got what I was trying to tell him and shook his head at the fact that someone had left it on as he leant over and switched it off and left.

What came next was the single most intense drug experience I have ever had.

As I lay back, my body began to feel lighter and lighter, till it felt like I was floating and the pain was a distant memory, but it was when I closed my eyes, the real show began.

As soon as I shut them, the ceiling I was once staring at transformed into a battleground, with a melee of random film characters, just like the battle scene at the end of Steven Spielberg's movie adaptation of Ernest Clines brilliant science fiction novel *Ready player one* but it was being played out upside down in 3D on the ceiling.

I could only put it down to a drug induced hallucinogenic type dream I was having, as my eyes were closed but it felt like I was witnessing this chaos as clear as day. It was amazing!

I could see elves and orcs from Lord of the rings, Freddy from nightmare on elm street, Jason from Friday the 13th, Mario, Luigi, and an array of other characters from the Nintendo games, World of Warcraft characters, the Dolorean from Back to the Future and the Big Foot monster truck were just a few of the figures creating carnage on the ceiling before me.

I just lay there enjoying the show, letting out little chuckles to myself with my eyes shut, till I eventually passed out.

A Small World

"Oliver...Oliver." I heard someone say in the distance. "Oliver."

It got louder, then I opened my eyes and there was a nurse standing over me.

"Oliver, I just need to put this on you," she said as she gently lifted my hand to put a wristband with my details on my wrist.

Standing next to her was a porter with a wheelchair in front of him. I noticed I'm no longer in my little pod but in a proper ward with other beds in and it was now night.

"The results of the lumbar puncture have come back and there were trace amounts of blood found in your cerebrospinal fluid. Now in some cases it can be from the initial needle puncture, but to rule it out we are going to take you for a CT angiogram scan, which is the same as a CT scan, but we will pump a dye through your system while we scan you to get a more defined picture, ok?" she explained in a very calm manner, "and Darren here is going to chauffer you," she added.

I just nodded, still groggy from the morphine, the pain was at a mild hangover level so not that bad.

I got off the bed into the wheelchair and was wheeled to the CT scan department.

It felt weird being pushed along in a wheelchair. It was my head that was the problem not my legs.

Oh well, if they insist, I thought.

When we got to the scan department, I was asked to take my jumper off by one of the scan technicians as she began to tell me about how the CT angiogram scan worked.

"Ok Oliver, what we're going to do is pump a dye into your canula which will go through your system while we scan you. Now, it's not going to hurt you, but you will feel a warm sensation as the dye goes around your system and it might feel like you've wet yourself when it gets to your waist area, but don't panic because you won't have, it's just the dye going through you."

I got on the scan table and she connected a tube to the canula in my right arm and told me to lie back on the table as she left the room.

As I lay on the table, I could hear the hum of the scan machine starting up, then I felt the warm sensation begin to course up my arm around my shoulders and head then down my left arm, then there it was, it had reached my waist and yep, it felt like I'd just pissed myself.

The table moved my head into the scan area for the scan. Five minutes later and I was all done.

I patted my groin area, just to make sure I was dry which I was, but it really did feel like I pissed myself.

I was wheeled back to my bed which I just laid on, updating my family and friends on the situation. I was wide awake now, the morphine was wearing off, the thumping hadn't come back fully, but I could tell it was in the post. I was given a sandwich and a bottle of water by one of the night nurses when I realised I hadn't eaten all day and was actually pretty ravenous.

The food and drink seemed to sober me up from the morphine and the pain started to return.

Here we go, I thought, when the doctor who originally saw me, returned with the most shocking news I'd ever had in my life. To say I wasn't expecting him to tell me what he did would be an understatement.

"Hello, Oliver, how are you feeling?" he began.

I told him the headache was back and he handed me some codeine with another brown pill.

"Oliver, I'm going to need you to take this as well as codeine. It's a drug called Nimodipine. The CT angiogram scan has shown that you have suffered a subarachnoid haemorrhage caused by an aneurysm; the Nimodipine will stop your blood vessels from spasming. I'm going to need you to take them every 4 hours, as advised by a specialist at the Walton centre in Liverpool, who we have been in touch with, as they are some leading experts in this field in the country. You will be transferred there first thing in the morning. I suggest that you arrange for someone to bring you some spare clothes. Don't worry, you are going to be in the best possible hands. Someone will be back in four hours to give you your next dose of Nimodipine."

In shock, I just thanked the doctor and he left me be. In that moment, the world became a small place. Everything around me tuned out and I just sat there in disbelief.

My heart felt like it dropped through my arse. *Fuck! A brain haemorrhage caused by an aneurysm, that can't be right. I know people who have had aneurysms and they're all fucking dead! Oh, shit, this can't be happening. I can't go out like this. I just can't.*

An aneurysm, for those of you that don't know, is a bulge in a blood vessel, a bit like a bulge you can get on say a bike inner tube, now that bulge can burst causing a bleed also known as a haemorrhage.

After having a minute to have a little melt down to myself, I snapped out of it and thought I can't put my family and friends through this, they'll kill me if I die now.

I texted my Sister and told her first and told not to worry, that everything was in hand, but that I needed some spare clothes.

Next was my Dad and Step mum, who couldn't believe the news, again I tried to play it down as much as possible which is hard to do. It's like telling someone a nuclear bomb isn't that dangerous.

I told them my sister was going to come round to sort me some spare clothes out. Next up was my brother, who was working off-shore at the time on an oil rig, so communication was patchy at best. He was very distressed by the news, but I told him I was going to fine.

Now, how was I going to tell my friends? It would have been be a ball ache texting them all individually, so there was only one thing for it - Facebook.

I put up a status, just to inform my friends that I was in hospital with an aneurysm, but was staying positive, and that I was in the best possible hands, and that I would keep them all updated and for my friends to support each other.

I realised it was not just me going through this now, it's all the people I care about going through it too, which is why I can't stand people who put cryptic status's up to blatantly fish for sympathy like, "Fuck my life in hospital again" for people to comment "omg what's wrong hope your ok hun" only to see a "pm u babe" in reply.

I mean for fuck's sake if you've got something to say then just say it!

The response I had from Facebook was overwhelming. I even had friends from twenty years ago giving me positive comments and each one made me want to tackle this thing head on.

My sister kept my core friends informed in a bit more depth as by then; everyone was really concerned about me.

It was about an hour and half later when a porter wheeled over a small suitcase which my family had dropped off at the entrance, as they were prohibited from seeing me due to covid.

After changing into some fresh clothes, I lay on my bed thinking thousands of thoughts about what would happen if I didn't make it through this, how was my family going to take it if I died, especially my brother and my sister, how would it affect them, also my dad and step mum.

I mean, my dad is in his seventies and has an underlying heart issue as it is, something like this could really make him ill. The guilt I felt was heavy and it made me determined to fight it. I just didn't know how. The nurse came around with my Nimodipine and Codeine, which would be the last one before breakfast. After I had the medication, I was left with my thoughts.

I didn't sleep at all that night.

In Good Hands

Morning came, and an ambulance was organised for me straight after I had some breakfast at about half eight.

They insisted I was wheeled to the ambulance in the wheelchair, despite my minor protest.

"Oh, if I must," I finally said to the porter and got in the wheelchair.

They really do treat their clients well at this hotel. I'll come here again, I thought.

We got to the ambulance within minutes, and I was transferred to a gurney and wheeled into the back of an ambulance.

A paramedic placed a blanket over me because my arms were strapped in like I was Hannibal Lecter. A paramedic sat in the back with me as we made our way to the Walton Centre.

She had short black hair and wore glasses, although she knew what my diagnosis was and why I was going to the Walton Centre, she didn't know how I came about to discovering my condition, so when she asked me, I went through my whole story to date from the previous Friday the 13th with her, which passed the time of the journey while taking my mind off the pain at the same time.

By the time I had told her my story, she was gobsmacked that I had left it 5 days before contacting, or even going to the Hospital, and told me that I was extremely lucky to still even be conscious enough to get help, let alone anything else.

We arrived at the Walton Centre, where I was handed over and taken to a ward where I had my own room.

The Walton centre is the only specialist hospital trust in the U.K dedicated to providing comprehensive neurology, neurosurgery, spinal, and pain management services. Their specialist staff offers a world-class service in diagnosing and treating injuries and illnesses affecting the brain, spine, and peripheral nerves and muscles. Their neurosurgery department is one of the biggest and busiest in the U.K. I really was in the best possible place I could be given my current situation. The room I was given was small but more than adequate. It was designed for a child, having a painting of a racing car on the wall, but it was nice and tidy with all the creature comforts I needed like a bed, T.V, drawers for my clothes, a little en suite toilet room. It even had a Playstation set up.

After I stowed my belongings away, a nurse came to take me for an MR scan, which was like a CT scan, as you lie there and go into a tube, but it is much louder, so loud that you are given ear plugs. It takes longer too, about quarter of an hour.

MR scan done and I was ushered back to my room. My head was pounding again and I must be due some painkillers soon.

Luckily enough, it wasn't long before a nurse came with some painkillers and my scheduled Nimodipine. She also took some bloods from me, which wasn't straightforward as it turned out.

The canula in my arm had been removed at Wrexham hospital before I came to the Walton centre, so they needed to insert a new one.

"I'm going to need to take a few blood samples I'm afraid, are you ok with needles?" the nurse said.

"Yeah, that's fine, you carry on," I said. *God, with all the poking and prodding I had endured this was going to feel like another day at the office,* I thought.

She stuck the canula needle into a vein next to the one the previous canula had been in, but when she connected the blood bottle to it, nothing happened.

"Oh," she said, "you're not being very giving today."

I apologised but she said, "Don't be silly, you must be pretty dehydrated."

I was, come to think of it, I'd only had a small bottle of water since the night before, when I was in Wrexham.

I grabbed a glass of water which was on the side next to a jug which was provided with the room. I drank the whole glass, filled it, and drank another half. I guess I was thirsty after all.

The nurse smiled and attempted to take the sample from the same place but in the opposite arm, but to no avail.

She then tried a vein in the back of my left hand, then my right hand. I was that dehydrated, I wasn't even drawing blood as the needle was going in, which I found quiet amusing.

The nurse, on the other hand, started to panic because she needed these blood samples, but she didn't want to cause me any unnecessary pain.

"Oh, I'm so sorry, I'll try your arm one more time, then I'll leave it," she said.

I reassured her she wasn't hurting me and told her to keep going as long as she needed.

She put the canula back in my right arm, connected the bottle, and it filled with dark red blood.

"Thank god for that, that's never happened to me before," the nurse said, before telling me that she was also going to need a sample direct from my artery as well which would sting and sting it did.

She took the sample with a syringe and needle direct from an artery on the inside of my wrist.

After being sucked dry of my blood and feeling like a second-hand dart board, I lay back on my bed updating friends and family, and also replying to messages of positivity and encouragement that I was receiving from various people that I've known, or been friends with, over the years.

This kept my mind occupied.

While lying on my bed keeping up to date with all the messages, there was a knock at the door before three people entered: A lady and two gentlemen.

When they were all in the room, the last gentleman closed the door behind him.

The lady introduced herself as Cathy. She was a Neurovascular Advanced Nurse practitioner. Next, she introduced the two gentlemen with her.

They weren't wearing their medical kit but were dressed in smart office wear; all of them were wearing face masks. One of the men was a Neurosurgeon and the other was a Neuroradiologist.

"Do you know why you're here, Oliver?" she asked, in an almost condescending way, as if she was talking to a child.

"Because I've had a bleed on my brain due to an aneurysm," I replied.

"Yes, that's correct well done," she said her tone normal now.

It was only when they explained the full extent of my condition that I realised she wasn't being condescending at all, she was being genuine as people in this condition were rarely conscious, let alone coherent and functioning; this was serious.

She handed over to the Neurosurgeon to explain what had happened to me.

He told me I had suffered a subarachnoid haemorrhage caused by not one but two aneurysms, one on the anterior communicating artery and one on the left posterior communicating artery.

The reason I was getting the severe headaches was because the aneurysms had bled into the space between the brain and the skull. He then told me the plan of attack for treating me, which would be a coil embolisation of the artery, which involved feeding an almost microscopic platinum thread in through my groin, up a main artery to the arteries in my brain with the aneurysms, and coiling the aneurysm, preventing it from bleeding again.

This was the less invasive alternative to going in through my skull and clamping off the artery direct.

He ended the explanation with a disclaimer that the procedure could leave me with mobility issues and there was percentage of chance it could result in death.

After the lowdown from the Neurosurgeon, Cathy said, "I know it's a lot to take in, but do you understand what we propose to do?"

"I do," I replied.

"That's great, now we don't plan on doing the procedure till Monday when we have a full team here. Till then, we'll carry on monitoring you and giving you your Nomdipine every four hours with some painkillers. We'll get you on the oral morphine I think, to help manage the pain. You're doing really well though. If you're happy with everything I just need you to sign your consent," as she handed me a clipboard with a form on it and a pen.

I'm literally signing my life away, I thought, as I signed the consent form.

Consent form signed and action plan in place they said their goodbyes and left me to rest.

Like Glue

I sat back on the bed, just staring at the wall thinking, *Shit, two aneurysms! That's not good, that's not good at all, this really could be it and there's not a thing I can do about it. No, I'm not going down this rabbit hole of self-pity, fuck that!*

I grabbed my phone and texted my family with an update of the two aneurysms and the coiling procedure. I let them know I was being well looked after and that I was confident I was going to be fine.

Next up were my friends who were updated on Facebook. I explained that I was in the best possible place I could be and that I wasn't going down without a fight.

Again, the messages came in thick and fast, and it was hard to keep up with them all, but it was just what I needed to keep my mind occupied from the pain.

Resting wasn't the easiest as I had a nurse come and take my observations every two hours and I had to have my medication every four and that was round the clock.

The next day was pretty straight forward, got my meds every four hours and took some naps because that's the only way to sleep when you're getting round the clock meds and observation checks.

I had to give them their dues at the Walton Centre; the attention to care was second to none.

It was pretty boring when I wasn't messaging my friends or family, the only thing I could do for entertainment was go down to the vending machine, which I took full advantage of.

Sunday came and there was a pang of anxiety in me that grew as the day progressed. I was only one day away from the fight of my life.

I had a sick feeling in the pit of my stomach. Cathy came to see me just after I had my last meal on Sunday to explain what was going to happen the following morning.

It wasn't till the evening, when I was alone in my room that it hit me like a tonne of bricks; *this could quite possibly be my last living night on earth* I thought.

Everything changes tomorrow, even if I do survive, I might not even be me at the other end. I could end up a vegetable trapped in my own body.

Surviving with brain damage or any type of mind-altering impairment frightened me more than dying.

My mind, my thoughts, are what makes me me. If I survived and couldn't remember who I was, surely that would be the same as dying, in a sense of my old personality ceasing to exist.

I needed to get one last message to my siblings.

Now, me and my siblings have always been close. We've stuck together like glue regardless of our age gap. I'm the oldest of three siblings, my brother being 7 years younger and my sister 14 years younger. I'll remind you that I'm 40, so you can do the maths.

Mine and my brother Adam's mum passed away nearly twenty years ago, which naturally brought us closer as siblings. Our dad remarried and that's when our little sister, Louise, came along. Now, people try to say "Well technically she's only your half-sister" which is a fantastic way to piss me off because there's no half about it.

We consider all 100 percent of her to be our sister and that's final.

As you may be able to tell, I am overprotective of her. We both are. In fact, growing up, it was like good cop bad cop, as my brother would be really strict with her about everything, whereas I would let her get away with murder. So, with a sense of impending doom, I felt the need to get one last message to them both.

I texted my brother first and began with,

Brother if something happens to me tomorrow, I need you to promise me you won't be bitter about life coz of it, make sure you look after Louise and that she gets through it, tell her I'm sorry. My vision started to blur as my eyes welled up with tears before spilling down my face, but I carried on regardless.

Try to assess all factors of a situation before coming to any conclusions, have some kids be happy, tell them about me one day, approach situations with an open heart and know that l love you xx.

I felt I had to hand over the mantle of responsibility of the oldest brother with some last words of wisdom before saying goodbye, which was, without a doubt, the hardest thing I have ever done.

Next was my sister's text, which was short and sweet.

Hey babba, don't be stressing about me ok. Everything's going to be fine. I Love u xx

I felt guilty for lying to her about how I felt but I just couldn't put her through that pain, even though she is a young independent woman, I still see her as my baby sister, and I will protect her from harm at any cost.

Plus, I knew if something did happen to me the following day, Adam would be there for her and that she would eventually forgive me. After

I sent my texts, I laid back on the bed. As you can imagine, sleep was out of the question, so I spent my last night reminiscing about all the good times I'd ever had with my friends and family.

There were so many memories; it kept me occupied till I eventually passed out in the early hours of the morning.

The Fight of My Life

The White Room

The next morning, I wasn't given any breakfast as it was the day of my operation. I'd got over the shock and was at peace with what had to happen. There was nothing I could do about it apart from just get on with it.

It was about 9 am when a nurse came in and gave me a medical gown and a pair of pressure stockings to change into after I'd showered. I put on the medical gown, which you can only tie loosely around the back. Between my arse hanging out the back and the schoolgirl-like stockings there really wasn't a shred of dignity left.

There was a bed waiting for me in the hallway of the ward, after ungracefully climbing on to the bed, I was wheeled to theatre.

When I got to theatre, I was handed over to a team of anaesthetists. There were two females and one male in the room. The male told me that they were the anaesthetist team and that they would be putting me under and for me not to worry.

They were all wearing the heavy duty, double vented masks as opposed to the typical blue paper medical masks, but he told me that they were wearing them just as a precaution, as they hadn't received my covid test results yet.

As he was talking, the female nurses were each side of me sticking monitor pads on various parts of my body. The whole situation felt very surreal.

This was it; it was nearly show time.

I was just about to have the fight of my life and I wasn't even going to be awake for it.

Well, there's no turning back now, I thought, *let's do this!*

The male anaesthetist put a plastic mask on my face as I looked at him, his head upside down in my vision as he was stood behind me looking over me. "I'm going to count to 10 and as I do you'll begin to feel tired, just breathe normally, one…two…three…four…five…six…seven…eight…" And then darkness.

"Beep…Beep" is the first thing I hear and it's beeping at regular intervals. I slowly open my eyes and see a white blur.

I'm a little discombobulated to begin with, but my vision starts to focus, and I realise that I'm in a slightly sat up position on the bed in an all-white room with a big window in front of me, but it's tinted as if it's got a one-way mirror effect on it.

The room is illuminated by white square fluorescent light panels in the ceiling. I notice I have tubes and wires coming from the inside of both arms, the top of my right hand, and the top of both feet.

The next thing I notice is one of the surgeons to my left, male going by the build and hair, but his face is covered by a double vented mask and behind him, another figure sitting with their back to me, female I think, in front of them is a laptop which is on a stainless-steel trolley.

I can see part of the monitor; it has many graphs on it. The graphs look like they're moving in real time. Standing to the right of me is another male figure wearing blue scrubs, again also wearing a double vented mask.

The surgeon holds his hand out palm down above my left hand and asks me to lift my left arm. I slowly turn to him after acknowledging the figure to my right and complied, lifting my left hand till it touched his palm.

"Good," he says and then asks me to do it again, but tells me to push up against his hand, which I do, and when I push up against his palm, he pushes down against my hand, but I resist.

"Good, that's brilliant," he says and moves to the bottom of my bed and raises his right hand over my left foot and we repeat the procedure without any issues. When he gets to testing my right foot, I raise my foot to touch his left palm fine, but when he tells me to resist, he just pats my foot down on to the bed.

I try again, but with little effort he pats my foot back down. I start to panic, and I try to tell him that I can't do it, but all that comes out is a sort of groan.

That's when I realise there's something in my mouth stopping me from being able to talk.

The surgeon then moves to my right side to test my right arm, and again, I just don't have the strength to keep my arm up.

I start shaking my head to tell him I can't do it. I just can't.

Why can't I do it? I keep thinking round and round.

Meanwhile, the surgeon has turned to the figure in the blue scrubs and says something. I couldn't hear what is said as he moves to the bottom of the bed, while I'm just shaking my head at him, trying to tell him that something was wrong.

I could see the figure in blue to the right, in my periphery, he has a syringe, and he attached it to one of the tubes coming off my right arm, he presses the plunger on the syringe, and everything went dark again.

Beep....Beep came the familiar sound as I lay there a few moments before opening my eyes, a part of me hoping that it was all a bad dream and that I'd be at home in my own bed.

It wasn't to be, though.

I opened my eyes, and I was still in the white room. This time there was only one person with me. A short Asian lady, again with the duel vented mask on.

She introduced herself and asked me if I knew where I was. I nodded to her to confirm I did. "Don't be frightened of the type of mask I'm wearing, it's just because we haven't had your second Covid test result through yet, so please don't be alarmed. Also, please don't try to speak as you have a tube in your mouth helping you to breathe," she said as I just nodded to let her know I understood what she was telling me.

She carried on.

"The mobility in your right side was down to about thirty percent, this was due to a blood clot which had caused you to have a stroke during the procedure, but we were able to treat you straight away with aggressive blood thinners which should have dissolved the blood clot, that's what is going through a lot of the tubes connected to you. It's nearly 4 in the afternoon on Tuesday."

HO....LY SHIT! I thought. I'd had a blood clot and a stroke and it's a day and a half later.

As if she read my mind she continued with, "I know it's a lot to take in, but you are doing absolutely fantastic. Now that you're awake, do you mind if we do a mobility test?"

I shook my head, and she came to my left side and held her hand above my left hand.

I knew what to do so I lifted my hand till it touched her palm and she tried to push it down, but I resisted. We repeated the procedure with my left foot. Again, she tried to push it down, but I resisted. Next was my right foot. I lifted it to her palm and as she pushed down on my foot I resisted.

Yes, I'm doing it! I thought. "That's brilliant Oliver," she said as she moved to my right arm to repeat the procedure one last time.

I lifted my arm till the back of my hand touched the bottom of her palm and as she tried to push down, I held my hand there strong. *Get in!* I thought.

"Brilliant," she said. "Oh my god, you don't know how many people are going to be so glad of that!" she added.

She told me to just lie there and rest, but to be honest, there was nothing else I could do.

I have never felt as weak as I did then. I felt like I'd gone ten rounds with Tyson and Fury.

I noticed my headaches were gone, and it wasn't like the pain was subdued from painkillers, it just wasn't there anymore, which filled me with a sense of relief.

As I lay there resting, my mind was void of thought, which was a strange sensation to me. It was as if my brain was too exhausted to think.

Some time passed, how much I don't know, as I had no sense of time at this point, but a petit young lady in a white tunic came in. She introduced herself as a specialist nurse that was in charge of my respiratory therapy. She explained to me that she was going to remove the tube from down my throat, and that I was going to start breathing on my own.

She also told me that my throat may be a little sore for a while after it's removed.

As she grabbed the base of the tube in my mouth, she counted to three and pulled out the tube, which was not a nice thing to go through.

I felt every ridge of the concertina tube scrape along my throat. I held my breath as it was being pulled out, and thought I was going to run out of breath before it was all out.

I couldn't believe how long the tube was.

I coughed a few times once it was out and was handed water in a cup like a child's sippy cup, but it was clear with a straw in it.

I took a couple of sips of water which quenched and soothed my arid throat.

"Good, now I'm going to go through a breathing exercise with you, I just need you to follow what I say," she began as she stepped close to my side and put one hand each side of my chest as if she was about to lift me up, but she just kept her hands in place and asked me to take a deep breath in through my mouth as far as I could. "Good!" she almost shouted, like a sports coach would while training his all-star team. "Now take one last breath in through your nose."

I did what she told me, even though it felt like I couldn't breathe in anymore but, fun fact, no matter how much of a breath you take in through your mouth, you'll still be able to draw a breath in through your nose.

You just tried it, didn't you?

Told you.

I was rewarded with another "Good!" as she held my chest, analysing my diaphragm movement.

We repeated the exercise three times before she was satisfied. She told me to do the exercise every so often before she left. Not long after, a man wearing a face mask, in smart office wear, poked his head round the door and asked the nurse looking after me how I was doing.

"Brilliant, really well look," she said, as she motioned for me to lift my arms, which I did, "and look," she said as she motioned for me to repeat the process with my legs, which I did.

The gentlemen at the door let out a loud, "Yes!" as he fist bumped the air. "That's great. I just wanted to check on him before I went home," he said before leaving.

The nurse turned to me and said, "See, everyone is so pleased with you, that was Mani, he did the operation on you."

Still in a state of bewilderment, I just smiled at the nurse. I felt well and truly drained of energy and it's not long before I fell asleep, which of course, set off the oxygen saturation alarm because my sleep apnoea has kicked in and I hadn't got a tube down my throat breathing for me.

Here we go again, I thought as I remembered the palaver it caused at Shrewsbury Hospital at the beginning of the year.

"Oh, did you dose off?" the nurse said,

"Yes," I croaked out as this was the first time I had attempted to talk.

The nurse handed me the sippy cup and I took another slurp of water through the straw.

"We know about your sleep apnoea and it's important for you to get as much rest as possible, so I'm going to mute that alarm for you," she said as she pressed some buttons on a device attached to the top of my bed behind me,

"Thank you," I said, voice still raspy.

I.C.U

It was night when I was moved from, what I learned to be, a theatre room to the Intensive Care Unit. I was moved with my bed as I was still hooked up to loads of drips and monitors.

The I.C.U was a big ward with a long table in the middle and a row of beds each side of the room and across the bottom of the room.

I was put down the bottom end and there was someone in the bed next to me and two more people in the beds diagonal to my left.

Each patient had their own nurse dedicated to them who sat on a chair at the end their beds in front of a laptop and a stainless-steel trolley. I thought they were all sleeping before I learned that they were actually in comas.

I was handed over to my own personal nurse, or should I say the next nurse on shift. I was given a small pot of ice cream for my dry throat; the ice cream tasted amazing. It was like it was the first time I'd ever tasted it.

I was that weak, I noticed that I was holding the spoon like a child with my hand gripped around the handle in a fist.

I've never felt as vulnerable as I did lying there, needing assistance to do anything, and I mean anything, like going to the toilet, which was a challenge at best.

Having to piss was dealt with as I had a catheter in, which in itself was not very pleasant. It was when my bowels started to move which was the tricky bit. And start to move they did due to the laxatives they gave me post operation.

In fact, going to the toilet was an all-out tactical mission. As I was hooked up to various machines with wires and tubes it meant that I wouldn't be able to go far from my bed, so a mobile commode was wheeled to my bedside, the privacy curtain was pulled round, and with the help of my personal nurse, I had to negotiate myself on to the commode, trying not to pull on the wires and tubes coming out of every limb on my body.

I felt like one of those old-fashioned marionette puppets on string.

As I was on the commode, I thought about all the texts of support off friends near and far, and in particular the ones from some of the lads that I used to go out drinking with, whom I hadn't seen for years.

A lot of the texts said the same sort of thing, which was kind of like "Hope you get better soon mate, just think of all the sexy nurses you can crack on to" and in that moment I just thought to myself, *Really?! What do they expect me to do? Hit the nurse with a "Hey hot stuff how you doing, do you come here often?"* In my bright white schoolgirl like pressure stockings and a medical gown, which was just like wearing a giant bib, while she's got me bent over the commode wiping my arse for me?

Somehow, I don't think she would be that flattered, but I guess they meant well.

After I was all finished, I got back on my bed and had a little chuckle to myself at the scenario that I just played out in my head and felt a sense of relief, relief that I was still me, because only my warped sense of humour would think up a stupid scenario like that.

Then I realised that I'm actually starting to get my thoughts together.

My belongings were eventually brought to me by a porter and the first thing I did is text my family to let them know I'm ok and that I'm on the mend. After that, I put out a status on Facebook letting everyone know that I had the operation and was responding well to the treatment and that I was grateful for all the support and kind words I'd had off everyone.

As the medication in the drips finished, they were taken out. The ones in my feet were the first to go, followed by the ones in my hand and arms. This happened over a couple of days, and all the while I had round the clock care from a personal nurse.

I was getting stronger by the day and it gave me a lot of time to think about how lucky I was to survive and how close to death I actually came.

If I were a religious man and believed in god, I would have said this to him, "You horrible bastard, you nearly had me. I even said goodbye to my brother because of you, and talk about kicking a man while he's down, you throw a blood clot and a stroke in for good measure you absolute shit house! And as for orchestrating a pandemic so none of my family or friends could be with me during my hour of need, now that is some villainous mastermind forward thinking, I'll give you that, but fuck you very much, you're not keeping me down!"

But I'm not a religious man so I guess that's just addressed to the universe.

I do however believe in spirits, souls, and the afterlife which is why I believe that all my dearly departed family and friends, such as my mum, my uncle, my grandparents, and a handful of my friends had a part to play in why I'm here today.

I believe that they weren't ready for me to join them and that during my operation, all though there were complications and that I had come to terms with the fact that I might not survive, I believe they may have had an influence how I beat the odds of survival.

The High Dependency Ward

With all my drips finished, they were taken out, as was my catheter I was relieved that was over, I was given the bump up to the High Dependency Ward, which was a smaller ward with six beds in, three on each side with a washroom down the bottom.

As you came into the ward the first two beds on the left were filled, as was the first one on the right. I was put down the bottom on the right. Where you had one nurse to one patient in I.C.U here there was one nurse for the four of us, but they were posted in the ward 24/7.

Once I was in my new ward and got settled in, I was able to take a shower and change into some actual clothes.

It was obvious to the nurse that I was cognitive and able, but she still had to ask whether I needed assistance in the washroom, to which I respectfully declined.

I stood up from my bed and sat straight back down, this was going to be harder than I thought. My legs were so weak; I had been in bed for nearly four days straight.

I stood up again and steadied myself and started to shuffle my way to the washroom, which my bed was closest to luckily enough.

As I attempted to walk to the washroom, I noticed the pain in my groin area. It felt really tight and tender, especially the right side.

When I got to the washroom and took off my gown, I could see why I was sore. There was a bruise that covered the whole of the inside of my right thigh in multitude of colours from black to blue and even some yellow in there.

That's a hell of a war wound, I thought, *can't wait to show my mates.*

I turned the shower on and just stood underneath propping myself with one arm letting the shower rain down the back of my head and neck.

I felt each drop of water hit my skin, almost massaging, it felt amazing.

I think this was the first time I realised that I would have a better perspective on things and would learn to appreciate the simpler things in life.

After my shower, I got changed into some comfy clothes and made my way back to my bed, this time with a bit more ease as my groin had loosened since having a shower and moving about, but even that was enough excitement for my body because not long after I had to take a nap and I wasn't just tired; I **had** to sleep.

After my nap, I had a visit from three consultants. This was a daily update that every patient had. They were pleased with my progress and had booked me in for a MR scan so they could have a look at how I'm responding to the coils that are now filling the aneurysms.

After my lunch, I have another nap, which was beginning to be a theme, but I was feeling that little bit better after each one.

After my nap, I spent the afternoon messaging family and friends while watching daytime telly.

Each bed had a telly hanging from the ceiling, but the reception wasn't very good, it was ok for some background noise though.

Other than that, I spent the day just observing my surroundings, that and going for a piss every half hour. They were well on top of my fluid intake, and I had to drink 3 litres of water a day.

Back home I'd be lucky if a drank 1 litre let alone 3!

And with me recently having had a catheter in me I was finding it hard to hold it in, so I had to go to the toilet quite regularly.

The lad in the bed next but one from me looked to be in his late twenties, he had a medium build with pale skin and almost a beard, but I think that was more from lack of shaving than choice. He had short, cropped hair but with a patch which had been shaven a lot shorter, with a big cut in the shape of a 'C' in it which had been stitched closed.

He was having some sort of therapy with a nurse; she was assessing his mobility.

She had asked him to stand up and walk towards her.

He stood up and started to walk towards her slowly; being mindful of every step he took. It looked unnatural, as if he had to think about the movement before he actually did it.

Next, she filled a mug with water and asked him to hold it.

She passed him the mug with the handle facing him; he grabbed the mug off her but is unable to hold it steady, instead his hand shook profusely, spilling the majority of its contents on the floor.

I go back to looking at stuff on my phone, thinking I could have ended up in a worse state than that, and wondering how did I not end up like that poor lad?

The lad opposite him was eastern European, I think. He couldn't speak a lot of English and kept himself to himself.

The chap next him, which was diagonally opposite, was a chap called Dave. We'd said hello to each other but that was about it. He was an older chap, say in his sixties, skinny with dark and grey hair and a pale complexion. I think he was someone who had been in the high dependency ward a while from how familiar the nurses were with him.

He was quite chatty with the nurses and seemed a pleasant chap.

It was about 9 at night when they dimmed the lights for bedtime. I was pretty shattered from the day's excitement anyway, so I tried to get my head down.

It was about 1:00am when I heard Dave across from me shouting, "Julie?! Julie where are you?"

I grabbed the control on my bed and put it into a slightly sitting up position, so I could see what was going on.

Dave was sitting on the side of his bed and the nurse was walking towards him. "Shush, you'll wake everybody up. Now, what's the matter?" she said in a loud whisper.

"Julie you've got to help me get ready the boys will be here soon," he said.

"I'm not your wife David, I'm your nurse, Anne," she said as she put a hand on his shoulder trying to coax him back into his bed.

"What!? What do you mean? Where am I?" he asked.

"You're in the hospital David, but you're safe, you just need to get some sleep," the nurse replied as she lay him back down on to the bed and tucked him in.

Then he started sobbing. "I shouldn't be here, I shouldn't be here," he sobbed. "I need to go home," he cried.

It was a heart-breaking thing to witness, also a bit daunting to think of how frightening it must be for him not to know where he is and not to have his family around him.

The sobs eventually subsided, and he must have fallen asleep.

The next morning, I woke up at about 7.00 am. Between Dave's episode and having to get up again to take my 4 hourly Nimodipine, which the course was finishing in a couple of days, I was pretty tired.

I positioned the bed back in the sitting up position and saw that Dave was already sat up reading a paper as if nothing had happened.

The nurse swapped shifts and it wasn't long before breakfast came round.

Breakfast was a mix of cereal and toast which was brought round on a trolley by two dinner ladies.

"What you having Dave?" the one dinner lady asked.

"Rice krispies and some white toast please, love," Dave replied.

The dinner lady brought his breakfast over to him and he looked pleased as punch. "Thanks, love," he said with a big smile on his face.

I ordered my breakfast and as I sat on the side of the bed eating, I thought that's not the same man that was in that bed last night.

Physically it was but mentally it was a completely different man as he carried on throughout the day as if he had no recollection of the night before.

As guilty as it made me, I felt like the only sane person in a mental institute, and it wasn't through any malice it was just due to the fact that I was extremely lucky as far as the aftereffects of the operation. As far as I could make out, I had not suffered any permanent brain damage.

Don't get me wrong, I felt like I was in a constant daze and there was a cloud of fog in my head, but I still had all my faculties in order, and I was still aware of my surroundings and I could tell the fog was clearing as time went on.

I was feeling stronger by the minute.

I knew why I was where I was and apart from my groin area being sore, physically I was A OK. I just wanted to get out of there as there were obviously people in need of care and attention more than me.

That night, Dave went through the same trauma as he did the previous night, waking up in the middle of the night thinking he was at home then getting confused when a nurse responded to him and not his wife, till eventually crying himself to sleep, this occurred most nights.

Every day I felt marginally stronger. In fact, by day 3 of being on the high dependency ward, I was walking to another washroom which was just outside my ward in the hallway that connected all the high dependency wards on that floor.

I would walk there, all though with a bit of a limp, to have my shower and wash in the morning, so the guys in my ward could take their time using the washroom on our ward.

When getting my daily visit for an update the three people that came to see me were Cathy, the Neurosurgeon, and the Neuroradiologist. This time I could see their faces as they didn't have to wear face masks around me because I'd had the second Covid test result back and it was negative.

I sat up on my bed and Cathy asked me how I was with a beaming smile.

I told her that I felt ok all things considered.

"You look amazing," she said, "for the procedure you have been through you really do," she said.

"You had us worried there at one point, how is your right side?" the neurosurgeon asked.

"It's fine, my right hand had the shakes a little initially, but I think that was because a Canula needle was in it at the time, because it's fine now," I replied.

"That is fantastic, now could you close your eyes and hold both arms out like this," he said as he held both arms out straight in front of him, hands facing down.

I closed my eyes then held my hands out in front of me as if I were auditioning for a part as an extra on The Walking Dead.

"That's fantastic, Oliver, I'm really pleased with your progress," he said as I opened my eyes and relaxed my arms.

Cathy chimed in next with, "Ok, the next steps are to get you scanned so we can see if everything is ok inside, take some blood samples and make sure your blood attributes are levelled out as I don't know if you remember, but we had to put you on some aggressive blood thinners during your operation."

I nodded, "Yes, I remember being told," I said.

"Well, we need to just make sure your bloods are back to normal and all being well you'll be able to go home in a few days. How does that sound?"

I nearly welled up at the thought of getting out of there and going home. "That sounds amazing, Thank you for all you've done for me," I said to all three of them.

" You're welcome," they all said, nearly in unison.

"Now, someone will be round shortly to take you for a scan and to take some blood from you," Cathy finished.

I nodded and said, "Ok," and they all smiled and left.

As confirmed earlier, it wasn't long before a porter came to wheel me to the scan department. It felt a bit weird being pushed along to the scan room. I was pretty sure I would have been able to make it there on my own eventually, but it was insisted that I be chauffeured there, so who was I to argue.

Scan all done and back at my bed it was time for some blood samples which were taken directly from my arm as all the Canula's were removed.

The blood samples were a whole lot easier to give than previous attempts due to all the liquid I was being monitored to drink.

The fogginess in my head had cleared a lot but there was still a feeling of vagueness. It was such a weird sensation, but it got better with time which obviously meant I was healing, but the best way I can describe it is if you took away the pain of the worst hangover in your life, but left the shear strain of having to think.

I could feel my brain straining to think of the simplest of thoughts which seemed so odd as I always took thinking for granted, it was just something you automatically do isn't it? Well, not when you've had a team of Neurosurgeons digging away in your melon doing repairs.

Like my lung when it collapsed, now my brain is the second organ in my body that I took for granted and never really felt until I had that operation.

<u>Meanwhile, back at the ranch</u>

That Monday was terrifying for my family and friends. Everyone was on tenterhooks just waiting for some news, any news, of how my operation was going and then my Dad got the call from the Hospital late Monday afternoon, from one of the Neurosurgeons that operated on me.

He told him that there had been a complication and that I had suffered a stroke due to a blood clot and that, all though they were treating me with aggressive blood thinners, I may have lost movement in the right side of my body.

My Dad passed the update on to the rest of my family; My sister updated my friends and work colleagues. Everyone was devastated.

My Dad began to panic about my welfare when I was home as he was afraid he wouldn't be able to give me the care I needed, his main concern was how I would be able to get up the stairs and he was worried he wouldn't have the strength to lift me, which must have been heart breaking as a father.

My brother and sister calmed him down by coming up with a plan of moving my bedroom downstairs and everyone helping with my needs.

The panic was over the next day when my Dad got his next daily update on my progress and he was told that I had reacted extremely well to the treatment and that I had regained full use of my right side. It must have been such a relief for everyone.

Testing Time

A couple more days passed, listening to Dave sob himself to sleep, being made to drink an abundance of water and me getting stronger, so much so that I was able to leave the ward to go to the vending machine, or at least that's what I'd tell the nurse on duty I'd be doing, most of the time I would go for a wander around the hospital.

But that would only take up half hour to an hour of my day, the rest of the time I'd be back on my bed, in my bed, or sat on the chair or next to my bed.

I could tell I was ready for home as I was getting restless.

I had been in bed for just over a week, so you can imagine how relieved I was when Cathy came and told me that the scan and the bloods all looked good and that, after I did a little cognition test, I could go home.

She drew the privacy curtain around my bed and sat on a chair while I sat on the side of the bed facing her.

"Now, I'm just going to ask you a few simple questions, just so we can gauge where you're at with your recovery," she said as she handed me a piece of paper with some questions on it.

The first question was a memory test. There was the address Dave McCarthy, 24 Regent Street, Essex CB10 9LX written on the piece of paper.

Cathy said, "I want you to remember as much of the address as you can."

I nodded as she gave me a minute to try and memorise the address, then she covered the address with her hand and asked me what the second line of the address was.

"24 Regent street," I answered.

"And who lived there," she then asked.

Shit, I want to say Paul McCarthy but that can't be right, can it? He was a Beatle, wasn't he? Well, we are in Liverpool, so it could be right? No, it isn't. I'm over thinking it then it came to me, "Dave McCarthy," I blurted out.

Cathy smiled, "Yes that's correct."

She then pointed to a picture of a clock face which showed the big hand of the clock on eleven and the small hand on one. "Can you tell me what time that shows?" she asked.

I starred at the clock face knowing that under normal circumstances I would have been able to answer straight away but now I had to really think about it ."Ten to one," I eventually answered.

"That's right, It took you a minute to think about it though, didn't it?" she said.

I admitted it took me longer than it would usually

"This is why you will need to take things easy for a while. It will come back, but it's going to take time. Now, last test, how much money is there?" she said as she placed some coins on the bed next to me.

There was a fifty pence, twenty pence, two ten pence's, five pence, and three two pence pieces.

I starred at the coins and my brain tried adding them all up at the same time, not being able to come to answer.

That was the moment I realised that I wasn't a hundred percent.

I work with numbers all day. I should have been able to answer that question straight off the cuff, but I really had to break it down "fifty, sixty, seventy, eighty, ninety, ninety-five, plus six equals a hundred and one," I whispered out loud before answering, "one pound one p!"

Cathy smiled again and grabbed the change off the bed, "Yes, that's really good, I think you're ok to go home, but how do you feel?"

"Well obviously I feel a little banged up from the whole ordeal but I still feel more than ready to go home, I just want to be able to rest in my own bed" I said

"Oh I bet you do, right let me write up a discharge letter and arrange some medication for you and get you on your way" she said before leaving.

The Naughty Ward

I was so glad that I was going home. The first thing I did, once Cathy gave me the all clear to go home, was message one of my friends to come get me, then I messaged my family and told them I was coming home.

I packed all my stuff into my little travel case and sat on my bed anxiously waiting.

My lift wasn't going to arrive for another couple of hours but I was so eager to get out of there.

As I sat waiting impatiently, one of the porters and a nurse came over to me to tell me that I was being moved to another ward as they needed the bed.

I was led out of the high dependency ward to a ward at the bottom of the corridor, which was low dependency. As I got closer, I could hear various people talking and the atmosphere was completely different to the High dependency ward.

Well, there was an atmosphere to start with.

As I got there, one of the nurse's was laughing from being bantered with by one of the patients as she was leaving.

There were six beds in the ward, three on each side; the left three were occupied, as was the first one on the right. I was given the bed on the bottom right, leaving an empty bed between me and the guy on my right.

I just put my case on the bed and sat on the edge.

Now, although I was only in that ward for about an hour, I will always remember those four guys I met.

"Alright there la, where are yous from then?" the young lad in the first bed on the left said in a heavy scouse accent. I told him I was from Oswestry in Shropshire as I tried not to stare at his head.

He was a medium built lad with pale skin and ordinary features, apart from half his skull was missing, or that's what it looked like. The complete left side of his head was caved in, his head went from his ear to the top centre of his head at a 45 degree angle with a big scar that went around the edge of the indent. It was little bit distressing to look at.

"Where the fuck is that?!" he replied.

I just smirked. No body outside a 5-mile radius of Oswestry knows where Oswestry is. It's such an odd little place; it's like the Bermuda triangle.

"Go to Chester and head down," I said to him.

"What's your name?" he asked.

"Ollie," I replied and before I could ask him his name, he proceeded to introduce himself and the rest of the guys in the ward to me.

His name was James, the chap in the bed next to him was called Roy. Now, Roy was a big bloke, not so much tall but round, built like a hells angel and looked like one too! He was in his fifties, pale skin, bald, had a moustache and wore a patch over one eye. If I met him down a dark alley one night, I think the whole world would fall out my arse, but he seemed harmless enough under these circumstances.

In the bed next to him, which was directly opposite me, was Paul, Paul was the polar opposite of Roy, he was skinny short, again pale skin, with short grey hair and stubble. Paul and I were roughly the same age it turned out, and we went to some of the same night clubs around Liverpool back in the day.

And the last guy introduced to me, in the bed next but one to me was Simon. Simon was in a medical gown watching something on a laptop on his bed. He was a slender chap in his mid to late forties, he seemed to be educated and business orientated, unlike the other three his accent was different though, it was still scouse, but it was the old fashioned scouse accent, it was slower and more subtle, like Ringo Star from the Beatles.

After James introduced the rest of the gang, he asked me what I was in for, so I told him about my double brain aneurysm and explained the procedure I went through.

When I got to the bit about them going through my groin, James chimed in and said, "That's what he's got to have done but he's shitting himself," as he pointed to Roy laughing.

"Fuck that, they're not touching my bollocks," Roy objected, everyone burst out laughing.

I told them that they went in both sides of my groin and that I was fine.

He shivered and said, "Not a fucking chance, they can do it when I'm awake and all, they're not putting me to sleep, the nonce's," that was it then, the room erupted with more laughter.

"Why? Do you think the doctors are gonna touch you up or something? You silly fucker," Paul said.

"Well, I don't know, do I?" Roy replied.

From talking to Roy, I ascertained that he was there basically for the same reason I had been. He also had an aneurysm and although we were all having a laugh and joke about it, it was apparent Roy was genuinely worried about having the procedure done.

As I said before, I found out that Paul and I used to go to the same night clubs in the city back in the day, so this was some common ground we had to chat about. I noticed, when I was talking to him, that he was sitting with his back as straight as a board. It turned out that he had two discs removed from his spine.

He showed me the scar on his back, it was towards the bottom of his back in line with his spine, about six inches long and it was stapled shut. It looked very sore. He said he was on all sorts of painkillers and he was still in agony.

Simon's story was a bit different to the rest of us, as it wasn't head or spine related.

Simon took constipation to whole other level. He was supposed to be in another hospital not far from the Walton Centre. There were multiple specialist Hospitals around the Aintree area of Liverpool, and the one Simon was supposed to be in had no spare beds, which is why he ended up at the Walton Centre.

He'd had to go there to wait for a bed to come available at another hospital where they were going to have to operate on him.

Basically, he hadn't had any bowel movements for over a month.

"Yeah, he hasn't shit for over a month!" Paul interjected as Simon was telling me about his condition.

"Really?" I asked.

"Yep, 34 days now since I was able to go to the toilet, it's agony," Simon replied.

"I bet it is, have you not had laxatives?" I asked.

"Yeah, they give me laxatives before every meal and still nothing," Simon said before Roy chirped up taking the Mickey with:

"Hey, don't listen to him lad, he's full of shit!" and of course everyone erupted in laughter once again, Simon and all.

The rest of the room went quiet as James told his story.

He had been getting a lift somewhere with his mum in the car, she was driving, and he was in the passenger seat, when they had stopped at a set of traffic lights.

He wanted to get out and walk the rest of the way and said, "This will do," and began to get out of the car.

His mum hadn't heard him and was paying attention to the traffic lights which had just turned green, so she drove on as usual.

Now, because James had already started to get out of the vehicle, half in, half out, the motion of the car spun him around in such a way that when he hit the ground his head was in front of the back wheel of the car which tracked over his skull crushing it against the tarmac.

I got a sick, sinking feeling in my stomach as he was recounting this.

That really was one of those tragically life changing moments that happen in the blink of an eye. This is why I try to never bitch and moan about my situation no matter how bad it is because there are people who have gone through worse.

James continued his story telling me about how, in the hospital, as they were digging out the broken bits of skull, he wasn't allowed to be put under, but only had local anaesthetic, meaning he was fully conscious throughout, which is why they had to keep talking to him while they were doing it.

He gestured with two fingers pointing at his head just behind his eye where the 45-degree slope started. He then went on telling me how the police were trying to get him to press charges against his mum for grievous bodily harm.

Paul and Roy both chimed in with various expletives about the police, which I'm not going to mention, but I'm sure you can imagine.

James said his mum was devastated over what had happened as it was, and James knew, as tragic as it was, that it was an accident and no one was to blame, which is why it angered him when the police intervened trying to get him to press charges on his own mother.

The accident had happened about ten months prior. He had a metal plate put in his head, but his body started to reject it, so he had to have it removed, which is why he was there when I was.

He finished by telling me about his kids and how they tell him he's got a head like a Toblerone, this got a chuckle from me.

After he told me his story, he started getting changed to go out and buy some cigarettes. Paul was going to go with him when I realised that I had half a pack in my coat pocket.

Truth be told I had totally forgotten that I even smoked but going through what I did, and with smoking being one of the many potential causes of an aneurysm, although highly unlikely in my case as up until that point I only smoked 3-4 cigarettes a day, I thought it would be a good opportunity to give up, so I offered them to James who was very grateful for them.

"Sound that is lad, do you want some money for them?" he said to which I declined.

One of the nurses came in and told Simon that they had a bed for him at the hospital he's supposed to be at, so he left before me, but it wasn't long before my lift turned up.

When it did, I said my goodbyes to the lads in the naughty ward as I called it, got my prescription of drugs and discharge letter from the ward reception, and headed down to the entrance.

As I stepped outside, I took a deep breath of fresh air in and although I was shivering from the cold it felt good, I felt alive.

In fact, I felt the most alive I've felt in a very long time.

A close friend of mine had come to pick me up with her boyfriend and they met me at the entrance, and I got a big hug straight away.

It was so nice to see a familiar face it felt like home.

I then got a big bear hug off her boyfriend who was built like a lumber jack.

I was so pleased to see the pair of them.

We got my stuff packed away into the car and made our way home.

I spent the journey home retelling the whole story to both of them, starting from that fateful Friday the 13th.

An hour and half later and I was home.

My Dad was stood on the porch as we pulled into the driveway. I got my stuff out the car and embraced the two of them again, thanking them for the lift.

My Dad also showing his gratitude to them both and also thanking them as they left, and just like that, I was home!

The Aftermath

Finally being at home felt strange to begin with, looking back at my time in hospital and considering at one point I thought there really wasn't going to be a tomorrow for me.

It felt like my Dad and step mum were treading on eggshells around me, not really knowing how to deal with me, so I just assured them that I was capable of looking after myself. I just needed a lot of rest and I mean a lot of rest.

Well, for about the first month at least. It was incredible how much the whole ordeal had taken it out of me.

My physical endurance entailed taking the dog for a twenty minute walk and that would be it. I'd feel wiped out for the rest of the day and would have to take multiple naps.

There was still the feeling of being void of thought as well; I just didn't have the energy to think, so I didn't. I was to just relax and take it easy.

The doctors said it can take up to two years to fully recover from a brain aneurysm.

As time went on, the stronger I became, my thoughts started to build up as did my stamina. The body is an amazing instrument and you'd be surprised what traumas it can bounce back from.

After two months I had a video conference meeting with the Walton Centre to see how my recovery was going. They asked if I was having any headaches or blurred vision or pain anywhere, which I didn't. They even got me to do the zombie test on camera, so I closed my eyes and held out my hands in front of me.

They were amazed at the rapid rate that I was recovering at. They asked about my energy levels, which by that point I was able to stay awake all day, though I was sleeping in till about 10am.

They didn't think I would be ready for work for quite some time, but a few weeks later, I returned back to work, only on a part time basis, though.

Don't get me wrong, I didn't come out of the whole situation unscathed.

Every now and again I'll go to say something and it's something that I know I knew before the aneurysm, but I won't be able to remember the name of it. It's as if certain words have been taken from my memory bank, like they've been carved from my brain, but it's getting better by the day.

My handwriting has gone very untidy, almost childlike.

I used to have neat handwriting, having to write every day for work, whether it be filling out enquiry sheets or quoting on job cards, but now it looks like hieroglyphics on the paper.

I seemed to struggle writing the figure 8 the most, which is both odd and frustrating, knowing my capability of something and having to learn it again.

And then there's the pangs of anxiety I get every night, wondering whether I will wake up the next morning, thinking was that day just a bonus for me and tonight is the night I finally lay to rest. Which some of you might think is a dreadful thing to have to think, but again, it's getting better by the day.

But perceptively I see it as motive for life as well as a curse because the flip side to that sense of ever impending doom is that it has given me a new lease of life.

It's given me a sense of not wanting to waste one more minute of it.

I explained before how my brain was affected, that I couldn't remember certain words and how my handwriting has suffered, but something else happened to my brain and it's something I can't explain.

I have an urge to make certain accomplishments in life, one of them being completing this book, which incidentally I only started writing three months after my aneurysms. I have never been academic, nor did I do well in English at school and is something I would have never dreamed of doing before.

I've already published a couple of low content books while I've been writing this one to start learning about the industry.

I've started investing in crypto currencies.

Now I know that might not seem much of an accomplishment to most, but if you knew me before you would know I used to live hand to mouth and would never have any money left from month to month.

Yet now, since I've been in recovery, resting with all that time on my hands to revaluate my life, instead of watching stupid cat videos on YouTube like I was supposed to, I taught myself how to trade in crypto currencies.

It's like a beast inside me has awoken and wants to consume knowledge and succeed in future ventures.

All fear of new challenges now have gone, fear is unnerving and rattles you into complacency. You should never allow it to.

Keep your head down and plough forward as hard as it may seem, just do it one step at a time, one foot in front of the other and before you know it, you're beyond that scary place.

The more you challenge fear, the bolder you become, and you will be able to tackle any obstacle to the best of your abilities.

I still have a long way to go before I'm fully recovered.

There are still scans in store for me and a good chance that I will have to have another life threatening operation.

The coiling of the aneurysms was only an emergency fix because I had a bleed on the brain, to fix the issue permanently means going in again and putting a stent in.

A stent is a plastic like tube which would be placed on the vessel with the aneurysm completely blocking it off making it unable to bleed.

I don't know what the future holds for me, I do know I'm going to give it my best shot and face whatever challenges life throws at me head on.

If you've made it this far, I thank you for reliving what can only be described as the craziest year of my life and I hope I've given you a somewhat positive perspective on things.

I hope, if nothing else, you have been entertained.

Somebody once said, "Life begins at forty" and you know what? I think it does!

Dedications

I would like to dedicate this book to all the staff at the Walton Centre in Liverpool without whom I most certainly wouldn't be here. You are true miracle workers and do not get the recognition or credit you deserve. I thank you from the bottom of my heart for saving my life.

I also would like to dedicate this book to my mum, may she rest in peace, again without whom I wouldn't be here in more ways than one.

And last but by no means least, I want to dedicate this book to my family and friends who gave me strength to keep fighting. I love each and every one of you.

Web Links

https://www.oliver-morrison.co.uk

https://www.facebook.com/Twistedbookspublishing

Email: o.morrisonauthor@gmail.com